When Minutes Matter

EMERGENCY CARE ACROSS THE GLOBE

———

A collection of short stories, edited by Jennifer Jamieson and Rob Mitchell
on behalf of the Australasian College for Emergency Medicine and the
International Federation for Emergency Medicine

Hardie Grant

BOOKS

Acknowledgement of Country

The editorial team, along with the Australasian College for Emergency Medicine (ACEM) and the International Federation for Emergency Medicine (IFEM), acknowledge the Traditional Custodians of the lands upon which these stories were written and curated. We pay our respects to the Wurundjeri people of the Kulin Nation as the Traditional Custodians of the land on which the ACEM and IFEM offices stand, and to ancestors and Elders, past, present and future, for they hold the memories, traditions, culture and hopes of Aboriginal and Torres Strait Islander peoples of Australia. In recognition that ACEM is a bi-national college, we acknowledge Māori as tangata whenua and Treaty of Waitangi partners in Aotearoa New Zealand. ●

Dedication

This book is dedicated to all emergency clinicians across the globe, who deal with confronting situations every minute of every day. We also acknowledge the support of family, friends and colleagues, and the memory of those who are no longer with us.

———

Published in 2022 by Hardie Grant Books an imprint of Hardie Grant Publishing

Hardie Grant Books (Melbourne)
Ground Floor, Building 1, 658 Church Street
Richmond VIC 3121, Australia

Hardie Grant Books (London)
5th and 6th Floors,52–54 Southwark Street
London SE1 1UN

www.hardiegrant.com.au

Hardie Grant acknowledges the Traditional Owners of the country on which we work,
the Wurundjeri people of the Kulin nation and the Gadigal people of the Eora nation,
and recognises their continuing connection to the land, waters and culture.
We pay our respects to their Elders past and present.

Aboriginal and Torres Strait Islander peoples should be aware that this publication may
contain names and images of people who are deceased.

All proceeds received by ACEM from the sale of this book will be directed to
ACEM emergency care development initiatives.

A catalogue record of this book is available from the National Library of Australia.

When Minutes Matter: Emergency Care Across the Globe

ISBN 9781743799147

Publication commissioned by Courtney Nicholls
Publication managed by Hannah Louey
Publication project edited by Leanne Tolra
Edited by Jennifer Jamieson and Rob Mitchell
Cover designed by Josh Durham
Internals designed by Robert Bertagni
Printed in Australia by Ellikon Fine Printers

Australasian College
for Emergency Medicine

I F E M

"

Emergencies occur everywhere, and each day they consume resources regardless of whether there are systems capable of achieving good outcomes.

OLIVE KOBUSINGYE
Ugandan trauma surgeon and injury epidemiologist, writing with colleagues in the *Bulletin of the World Health Organization,*
August 2005

From the editors

One of the drawbacks of practising emergency medicine is that a patient is only in your care for a limited time. In fact, in some countries, an indicator of hospital performance is the efficiency with which a patient can be assessed in the emergency department and then discharged or admitted.

But every patient who receives emergency care, no matter how briefly, leaves behind a story. This book recounts a small number of them, from within and beyond the emergency department.

On healthcare's frontline
As emergency clinicians, we frequently encounter individuals experiencing profound distress. Many of our patients are acutely unwell, requiring urgent assessment and care. We also meet their loved ones, and share in their concern, hope and grief.

In these periods of stress and uncertainty, patients and their families place trust in us to advocate for them. We are relied on to provide immediate treatment, but also facilitate access to ongoing care, whether in the operating theatre, the intensive care unit, the hospital ward or the community.

Outside of the resuscitation environment, emergency clinicians regularly look after patients with complex social and mental health needs, who would otherwise be unable to access the support they need. We take pride in providing care to anyone and everyone – irrespective of their age, their condition or their background. In many respects, the emergency care system is society's safety net.

The patients and families we meet often leave an indelible impression; their stories of illness and injury – and their resilience – forever ingrained in our memories. We are privileged to connect with them in such raw and sensitive circumstances, when physical and emotional vulnerabilities are laid bare. Humanity thrives in these unobtrusive moments.

In the many and varied manifestations of our work – from time-critical resuscitation to gentle conversations around end-of-life care – *minutes matter*. This book is a celebration of the compassion and empathy that are central to the delivery of emergency care.

A global perspective
It is timely to reflect on the unique responsibilities of emergency clinicians, and the value of emergency care more broadly. The COVID-19 pandemic has exposed human suffering and hardship on an unprecedented scale,

highlighting the entrenched inequities that exist across the globe. It has revealed the limitations of health systems, both resource-rich and resource-limited, and stretched healthcare capacity in almost every corner of the world. These impacts have cast a spotlight on the essential role of healthcare workers, and the individuals – laboratory scientists, epidemiologists and cleaners among them – who enable their contribution.

As we look beyond the pandemic, there is a strong imperative to share the experiences of emergency patients and clinicians from across the world. Their stories – of trauma and of survival – can help us imagine a different future, where access to quality healthcare is universal, and emergency care is considered a right and not a privilege.

This book, produced by members of the global emergency care community, aims to introduce you to the clinicians who deliver essential, time-critical care every day. We hope it provides an insight into their work and their humanity, and the highs and lows of clinical practice on healthcare's frontline.

In particular, *When Minutes Matter* aspires to amplify the voices of clinicians from low- and middle-income countries. These are the unsung heroes of global health; humble but deeply committed nurses and doctors working tirelessly to care for their communities. Although emergency care systems are underdeveloped in many parts of the world, the stories in this book demonstrate the depth of capacity and the opportunities for growth that exist in every corner of every country. We trust that it will bring meaning and momentum to the global emergency care development agenda.

Finally, we hope that this book highlights the deep sense of solidarity and shared experience that comes with being an emergency clinician. The authors come from a broad range of countries, cultures and contexts, but their stories convey a commonality that belies their diversity.

Emergencies occur everywhere
When Minutes Matter profiles emergency care at its best and at its most tragic. The pages will transport you across continents, from the harsh Australian outback to the darkness of Antarctica, and from isolated islands of the Pacific to the volatile streets of Palestine. There are critical messages about the social determinants of health, the construct of humanitarian aid and the impending devastation of climate change.

But the stories also convey a strong sense of hope for the future. We hope they serve to challenge, inform and inspire you. •

Dr Jennifer Jamieson and Dr Rob Mitchell

From the Australasian College for Emergency Medicine

As these stories of global emergency care started to trickle into our inboxes, we were curious: how much would we – who practice in senior medical roles in well-resourced emergency departments in Australia and Aotearoa New Zealand – recognise in the working lives of our colleagues in other places? The breadth and scope of this project, which has resulted in this wonderful book, was a stark reminder that even the best-travelled among us sees only a glimpse of the world and its people.

Then we started to read. We found ourselves transported, in time and place, to different climates and cultures, but the people and contexts felt inherently familiar.

It was immediately clear that we were among friends. There are common threads that bind emergency care practitioners across the globe – skill, empathy, creativity, courage and humanity.

We hope you enjoy this book, which demonstrates the power of stories to build understanding, to unite and inspire.

We give enormous thanks to everyone who has shared their stories, and to those involved in curating them. ●

Dr Clare Skinner
President
Australasian College for Emergency Medicine

Dr John Bonning
Immediate Past President
Australasian College for Emergency Medicine

From the International Federation for Emergency Medicine

Those of us living in places with established emergency medicine specialty physician training, and emergency care systems, understand that the emergency department is the front door through which access to unscheduled emergency care is available whenever it is needed. Yet globally, the burden of disease potentially amenable to pre-hospital and facility-based emergency care is estimated at a shocking 54 per cent of the annual deaths in low and lower-middle income countries (World Bank 2017).

Since the earliest days, visionaries have worked to improve clinical emergency care in their own hospitals, regions and nations, championing every step and collaborating with like-minded clinicians and leaders. This dedication eventually led to the formation of the International Federation for Emergency Medicine 30 years ago as a mechanism to enable global problem solving and collaboration for improving emergency care. IFEM's vision is creating a world where all people, in all countries, have access to high-quality emergency medical care. Today, more than 800 volunteer emergency physicians and a very small staff work within IFEM towards the goal of universal high-quality emergency medical care through developing education and standards, sharing expertise and friendship, and promoting the creation and growth of the specialty of emergency medicine in every country.

Why are we so passionate about emergency care? Why do physicians, nurses and colleagues come in shift after shift to face overcrowding, stress, time pressure and the emotional roller coaster that emergency departments can be? Is it making a difference to someone every day, being under challenge to be the best clinician possible due to the huge variety of cases we see, working with great teams, being a key part of a health system, or something more?

I am honoured to write a foreword for this collection of global stories where the answers to these questions are writ large on every page. The stories are an honest, often inspiring, at times confronting, account of the delivery of emergency care around the world. Whether they describe mundane day-to-day challenges or heroic life-saving moments, it is people who are the heart of emergency medicine. I thank the ACEM team for their vision and intense work to bring this together, and I thank every contributor whose compassion, commitment and drive shines on every page. ●

Professor Sally McCarthy
President
International Federation for Emergency Medicine

CONTENTS

PART 1
EVERYDAY EMERGENCIES
Stories of courage and compassion
from around the world

04
AUSTRALIA
Katrina Starmer

12
SOUTH AFRICA
Sa'ad Lahri

20
UNITED KINGDOM
Heidi Edmundson

28
AUSTRALIA
Petra Niclasen and
Ina Schapiro

36
SUDAN
Nada Hassan Ahmed Abdelrahman

44
TUVALU
Aloima Taufilo

54
TANZANIA
Alphonce Nsabi Simbila

62
AUSTRALIA
Tileah Drahm-Butler

70
ANTARCTICA
Meg McKeown

PART 2
CRISIS AND CONFLICT
Reflections on disaster, the pandemic
and emergency response

78
BANGLADESH
Evan O'Neill

90
AUSTRALIA
Amaali Lokuge

98
AOTEAROA NEW ZEALAND
Kelly Phelps

106
PALESTINE
Natalie Thurtle and
Mohammed Abu Mughiasib

118
MYANMAR
Rosanne Skalicky

126
INDIA
Ankur Verma

134
HONDURAS
Killiam Argote-Araméndiz

142
SRI LANKA
Harendra Cooray

150
FINLAND
Amy Neilson

PART 3
INSPIRING INDIVIDUALS
Profiles of clinicians who are leading
change in their communities

160
VANUATU
Vincent Atua

170
UGANDA
Justine Athieno Odakha

178
BRAZIL
Jule Santos

184
KIRIBATI
Brady Tassicker and
Fatima Mwemwenikeaki

192
GHANA
Joseph Bonney

198
PAKISTAN
LaiHeng Foong

206
PHILIPPINES
Maria Salud Loreen Cadiz-Kern

214
PAPUA NEW GUINEA
Wilma Sebby

222
AUSTRALIA
David Caldicott

Acknowledgements **230** ● Photography Credits **232** ● Abbreviations **236**

PART 1

EVERYDAY EMERGENCIES

*Stories of courage and compassion
from around the world*

Kerry Suapi (left) and Australian volunteer
Sarah Bornstein at St John Ambulance in
Port Moresby, Papua New Guinea. Sarah
was supported by the Australian Volunteers
Program to volunteer as an ambulance
clinical support officer in 2019.

Katrina Starmer crosses a dirt airstrip in Far North Queensland.

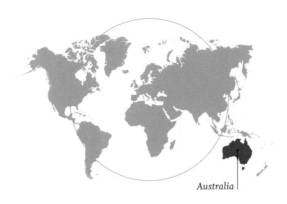

Australia

Night flight

KATRINA STARMER

Katrina Starmer is a mother of four and an emergency physician at Cairns Hospital in Queensland, Australia. She is also completing a fellowship with the Australian College of Rural and Remote Medicine through the Royal Flying Doctor Service (RFDS).

The sky is darker than usual tonight. A silver moon sometimes keeps us company, but mostly we work in silence and isolation in the aircraft, our mission unknown to the people in their beds beneath us. A natural camaraderie forms between doctor, nurse and pilot on an RFDS night shift. Something draws us together, whether it be a shared desire to be at home asleep, or the excitement of a mission to help someone we have never met.

Tonight's patient is a Queensland National Park ranger named Craig. We've heard a little about his story from the referral phone call, received at 5pm this evening.

On his rostered day off, Craig was fishing from rocks in a remote part of Cape York when he was suddenly and viciously attacked by a crocodile. The crocodile launched out of the water and tore into his thigh with its teeth. As he fell to the ground, realising he was about to be taken into a death roll, Craig jammed his thumb into the crocodile's eye, desperate to pry himself free.

The crocodile, almost three metres in length, then took a second lunge, clamping down on Craig's hand, degloving it from the wrist. Somehow, Craig wrenched his hand free from the crocodile's mouth and managed to straddle the animal, holding its jaws shut in an awkward embrace. As they paused, each pondering the other's next move, Craig was able to lift the animal's closed jaws off the rocks and lever it into the ocean.

Ironically, Craig had been wearing trademark 'Croc' shoes at the time of the incident and, perhaps unsurprisingly, these had floated off into the water during the scuffle. He later told me that his first thought in the aftermath of the incident was not, 'Thank goodness I'm alive' but, 'Oh dear, I've lost my shoes'.

Craig scrambled away from the bank and stumbled to his car, bleeding and shocked. He drove for an hour along a remote dirt track to the ranger's station where his colleague was waiting. At that point, the RFDS was contacted.

It was clear from Craig's description of the events that his injuries were potentially limb threatening. While preparing for take-off, we prescribed some pain relief from the RFDS medical chest in the ranger's station. This robust metal box is provided to cattle properties and remote outposts across the country. It is stocked with drugs such as antibiotics, morphine and paracetamol as well as dressings. Craig took the medication, his colleague bandaged his hand, then they drove for a pain-filled hour to reach the nearest dirt airstrip. This was where we had arranged to meet.

> Somehow, Craig wrenched his hand free from the crocodile's mouth and managed to straddle the animal, holding its jaws shut in an awkward embrace.

For our RFDS team starting the night shift, this was a 'priority-one' retrieval. It takes around one and a half hours to fly the 800 kilometres from Cairns to Bramwell Station. It is just as well we can't get there immediately because the station owner needs an hour or so to muster a mob of cattle off the airstrip. She also needs time to turn on the solar lighting to transform the dirt paddock into a night runway. In the past, RFDS planes landed by the headlights of a couple of four-wheel-drive vehicles. Changes to workplace health and safety regulations, however, mean that runways must now be lit along their length with either solar or kerosene lamps. In rare cases, long rows of fuel-soaked toilet rolls are required.

ABOVE LEFT: Craig with the RFDS crew on the night of the accident.

ABOVE RIGHT: An emergency landing strip for the RFDS in outback Australia.

It is an incredible experience to cut through the expansive darkness of the night in a small plane and see the first flicker of light from the bush runway lanterns. As the ground grows brighter and slowly comes up to meet us, I see piles of cattle dung littering the red earth.

The landing is incredibly smooth – a credit to the station owner for their runway upkeep, and the flying expertise of our senior pilot, Phil. We come to a halt as the engines are turned off and call out 'Clear door!', as the stairs of the plane gently touch the ground.

We meet Craig in the dark, near the tail of the plane, and usher him into the white light of the cabin to assess his injuries. He estimates that he has lost around half a litre of blood and is mainly concerned about his right hand. As the dressings are removed, tendons and vessels and the fan-like fibres of tiny hand muscles come into view. It looks like a diagram from an anatomy textbook.

We clean and dress the hand, and then move onto his leg injuries. Some of these are still gaping and oozing blood. One is uncomfortably close to the femoral artery. Flight nurse Katy and I again clean and dress the wounds, then reinforce them with compression bandages to stop the bleeding. At this point, a Queensland Ambulance Service paramedic arrives after a two-hour drive from Bamaga in the north. He assists us with equipment and supplies before bandaging puncture wounds on Craig's leg, which are decorated with small blebs of fat and soft tissue. We hang intravenous fluid and antibiotics, administer pain relief and then 'package up' Craig for the retrieval back to Cairns Hospital.

A motley crew
Craig's journey, however, is far from over. First, we must detour via Aurukun, a nearby First Nations community, to pick up a patient who has potentially been bitten by a snake. Thankfully she is not desperately ill, and we can rapidly lift her onto the aircraft in a stretcher, positioning her across the narrow aisle from Craig. Her snake-bite pressure bandage has already been applied, and she quickly falls asleep under the comfort of a blanket.

It is 11pm by this point and most people in the Aurukun community are asleep. As Katy checks the aircraft door locks in preparation for take-off, I peer outside into the darkness and consider this unique situation. We are quite a motley crew – pilot, nurse, doctor, a park ranger with injuries from a crocodile, and a patient bitten by snake – all on a midnight tour of Cape York.

We are quite a motley crew – pilot, nurse, doctor, a park ranger with injuries from a crocodile, and a patient bitten by snake – all on a midnight tour of Cape York.

A second stop in the small country town of Coen is needed to re-fuel the aircraft. The distances across Cape York and many parts of remote Australia are so vast that planes often need to plan stops at re-fuelling sites in the middle of the outback. It is midnight now, and the Coen re-fueller appears in his pyjamas to help. This job is often allocated to local community members who have received special training. In some small Cape York communities, there are no full-time airport staff.

Despite his discomfort, Craig does not complain about either of the detours. His only annoyance is that, on take-off, he cannot equalise his ears with bandaged hands. I press on his nostrils for him – it's all part of the retrieval service, I explain.

On arrival back in Cairns in the early hours of the morning, an

ABOVE: Katrina
Starmer and
colleagues in the
back of an
RFDS aircraft.

ambulance collects Craig from the tarmac at the RFDS base to take him
to hospital for surgery. The patient from Aurukun is also transported to
the emergency department where she will be treated for her snake bite.
As the paramedic loads the final stretcher into her truck, she remarks
how quintessentially 'Australian' this retrieval is.

It strikes me that the sense of teamwork within the plane extends
beyond the immediate crew. This retrieval has required collaboration
between many generous and community-minded individuals across
Cape York: the ranger who drove his bleeding mate on a rough dirt road;
the station owner who spent the evening preparing her private runway;

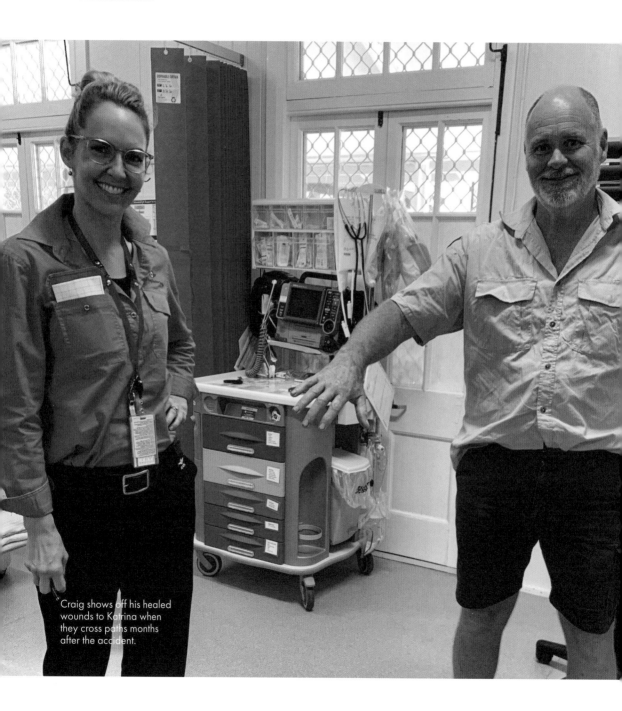

Craig shows off his healed wounds to Katrina when they cross paths months after the accident.

the Coen re-fueller who left the comfort of his bed at midnight; and the paramedic who drove two hours from Bamaga to meet the plane. It is a living testament to the resilience and cooperation of the people who live and work in the bush.

Forever dedicated

As a mother of four I did not expect, at this stage of my life, to be flying around remote Australia in the middle of the night. Neither did I expect so many other people to be up and about ready to help the RFDS transport critically ill patients. In many instances, as on this occasion, these are people who have never met and may never meet again.

> ❝
> I share Craig's story to perpetuate the positivity that I felt witnessing this humbling humanity and inspiring teamwork.

Funnily enough, the story does not end there. I randomly met Craig again about six months later – at a COVID-19 symptom screening checkpoint in Far North Queensland. He was back working as a ranger and had called in to the small town of Chillagoe, where I was working as the local RFDS doctor. We laughed and exclaimed that we that must stop meeting like this! His hand looked remarkably good after multiple operations and skin grafts. We took an appropriately 'socially-distanced' photo; I signed his paperwork, and he continued on his way.

I am grateful to have met Craig, and to have been part of a spontaneous team of professionals and community members who came together to deliver world-class care to a fellow human being. I share Craig's story to perpetuate the positivity that I felt witnessing this humbling humanity and inspiring teamwork. ●

ACKNOWLEDGEMENTS
The RFDS wishes Craig all the best for his ongoing recovery and the important work he does as a ranger for his community. Craig provided consent for his story to be shared.

Corrugated iron shacks in Khayelitsha.

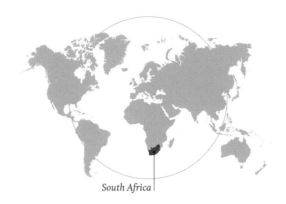

South Africa

A golden moment

SA'AD LAHRI

Sa'ad Lahri was born in Mokopane, South Africa and worked at Khayelitsha Hospital from 2012 to 2021. He is currently an emergency physician at Tygerberg Hospital in Cape Town and President of the College of Emergency Medicine in South Africa.

WARNING: This story contains references to paediatric deaths

On an ordinary day in Khayelitsha, two innocent boys trotted off to the barbershop with their proud mother. They requested a 'clean-cut', the latest look. Home they went afterwards, boisterous and happy. With a loving touch, their mother moisturised their clean-cuts using oil.

And then the explosion happened. A paraffin stove heater had caught alight, triggering the detonation. Their mother desperately tried to douse their bodies with water, the two boys screamed in pain and a fire, hot as hell, consumed them.

Khayelitsha is an impoverished, crime-ridden township on Cape Town's outskirts. It is a society in which the rich and the poor are utterly divided.

Residents of Khayelitsha live in makeshift structures made of sheet metal and corrugated cardboard, locally known as shacks. Meanwhile, a 30-kilometre drive leads you to Cape Town's wealthiest suburbs. This inequality is primarily driven by high unemployment, and the segregation that has persisted since apartheid.

Stepping inside the resuscitation room, I saw our traumatised emergency medical providers, the two boys and their petrified mother.

I immediately entered emergency medicine mode. Being composed, strategic and decisive – these are critical characteristics of an emergency physician. There was no time to be fragile in this moment. In fact, our training has taught us to be 'antifragile', meaning we thrive and stay strong even in the face of adversity.

As I arranged the doctors and nurses into strategic roles, I felt a tap on the shoulder. A more senior colleague had appeared to offer me advice. As a junior consultant, I had little experience in treating children with burns.

'Sa'ad, please tell the mother to kiss her children. The burns are too severe, and I don't think they will survive.' I think the nurses also knew, as they undressed the boys with utmost care. Both boys had full-thickness burns from head to toe. The charred, waxy and leathery skin on their bodies cracked every time they moved. I do not consider myself to be anxious, but the severity of the burns made me shudder.

> 'Sa'ad, please tell the mother to kiss her children. The burns are too severe, and I don't think they will survive.'

My colleague was urging me to prioritise kindness and empathy. But deviating away from the reassurance of traditional resuscitation did not make sense to me at that point. I had not yet even established intravenous access, and now I would have to give up. On reflection, however, he was not asking me to stop care, but to provide a 'golden moment' amid the traditional hour of resuscitation.

One of the boys mumbled something to his mother. He spoke in iXhosa, the local language. 'Tell these white people to save me. I also want to be a doctor.' My eyes met hers as I approached. 'Ma, I think you should go spend some time with your boys. They are extremely sick.' I didn't tell her that they were probably going to die, and that this would be her last moment with them awake. Did I do her justice?

She kissed them on the forehead, sobbing. Through the gaps created

ABOVE LEFT:
An emergency
department
equipment cabinet.

ABOVE RIGHT: A
patient receives an
intravenous infusion.

by the open curtains, I watched as she said her goodbyes. Her words looked to have eased their pain. The boys looked calmer. She slumped over in tears. I wasn't supposed to be emotional; I had to be strong. I had to be brave.

Both children underwent escharotomies - skin incisions to allow the underlying tissues to swell - of their thorax, upper and lower limbs. The face of one of the patients was also burned. That required an escharotomy too, but I did not know how to do it. Was it really necessary? I decided to leave his face alone. I could not bear to proceed.

I remember my trembling hands as I cut through the skin. The resuscitation was chilling but, somehow, I found the poise to perform the procedure cleanly and smoothly. The children were already burned, and I didn't want to complicate matters further with substandard incisions.

To provide the boys with the best care, we transferred them to a burns hospital. It was the right thing to do - to keep fighting, even though it seemed impossible. We could not show any vulnerability, especially to the patients' mother - she had heard her son ask us to save him. In retrospect, perhaps showing vulnerability would have been the more courageous choice. I was able to find critical care beds, which are incredibly scarce. Despite all the despair, there was also a false sense of hope that day.

"
There is no greater gift than the opportunity to care for a child, to help them achieve their dreams and their goals. Children teach and remind us of the fundamental needs of human beings – love and safety.

We followed up religiously with our colleagues at the burns centre and received an email thanking us for our 'outstanding efforts' as the young boys fought on. But a call a week later brought the devastating news that they had died. On that day, I felt sad for many reasons. What more could we have done? Should I have been more direct with the boys' mother regarding the prognosis? Could we have given her more time with her children?

Those young boys' injuries were the direct result of poverty, spatial apartheid and disadvantage. Their hope rested on the same 'white people' who designed the system and created the unequal society in which they lived.

The future the boy pictured – becoming a doctor – reflected a desire for education, the most powerful tool that exists against the cycle of poverty. Colonial legacies, biases and racial discrimination continue to impact healthcare. In this milieu, what is our duty? My view is clear – to be all that we can be, we must train, educate and empower the next generation to be better than we are.

There is no greater gift than the opportunity to care for a child, to help them achieve their dreams and their goals. Children teach and remind us of the fundamental needs of human beings – love and safety. I hope that those young boys knew that we cared deeply. •

Emergency department staff
transfer a critically unwell patient
in Madang, Papua New Guinea.

Beaches and coastal headlands of County Antrim in Northern Ireland.

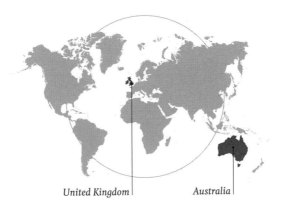

United Kingdom *Australia*

The path to belonging

HEIDI EDMUNDSON

Heidi Edmundson is an emergency medicine consultant at the Whittington Hospital in London, United Kingdom. She is a passionate advocate for staff wellness and runs programs that create connections.

For many people, practising emergency medicine is all about the drama – trauma cases, severed limbs and life-and-death decisions. But, for me, it's more than the razzle dazzle. It's about the gentler moments. Those times when our outer layer, our armour, falls away and a glimpse of the person inside, and our humanity, is revealed.

After a couple of years of working as a junior doctor, I encountered a stage in both my professional and personal life where I felt lost and directionless. So, with no proper plan in mind, I moved from Dundee in Scotland, where I had been a medical student, to Preston, just outside Manchester in England, to do emergency medicine. It's the job that everyone does while they wait to discover what they really want to do. In those days, it was called 'Accident and Emergency'. The few plans I had disappeared with the sudden death of my father. He was one of those men who die suddenly, unexpectedly and in the middle of a task that they will never get to complete. In his case, it was packing to help me move house.

So instead of him coming to help me, I ended up going home to Ireland for his funeral. It was the first dreadful thing that had ever happened to me.

After his burial, I was at a loss as to what I was supposed to do next. There was no rule book, no map. So I went to Preston, to work, just one week later than planned. We hear a lot about the life events that cause the most stress - changing jobs, moving regions and experiencing the death of a close family member. At the age of 27, I experienced all three simultaneously.

Everyone in my new workplace showed me care and love. They held me together through that first hard year of grief. I look back on that time with great affection. Something about the chaos and confusion of the department matched my own inner turmoil, as I struggled to make sense of my grief and my place in the world. If I focused on the external, I did not have to deal with the internal.

I found the emergency department a comforting environment and, in that year of loss, somewhere that I felt safe and secure.

My disconnection gave me a kind of freedom. There and then, I decided that the way to deal with all I was feeling was to go away as far as the sea could take me.

After I had been there for just over a month, they gave me a fortnight's holiday. As it drew nearer, I felt a sense of dread. Spare time is the enemy of those trying desperately to keep busy and avoid thinking.

I went back to Northern Ireland to see my mother and sister. It was a strange time, all of us grieving in our different ways and at different paces. Grief separated us and locked each of us in our own rooms, physically and emotionally.

One afternoon, I took a walk on the beach. It was a perfect September day, bright but chilly, my father's favourite time of year. As I walked, a disorientating feeling that I did not belong anywhere engulfed me. I no longer knew where to call home. It was a sickening feeling, like plummeting suddenly on a rollercoaster. A sense of belonging was never something I'd been conscious of, but now its absence left a jagged hole inside me. I felt incomplete.

As I looked out at the sea, I recalled being told as a child that it went all around the world. The waves breaking here may have once broken on the sand of some faraway place. I realised the sea did not belong anywhere - and at the same time, it belonged everywhere. So, perhaps, I could also

ABOVE: Ambulances outside an emergency department in the United Kingdom.

belong everywhere. My disconnection gave me a kind of freedom. There and then, I decided that the way to deal with all I was feeling was to go away as far as the sea could take me.

A year later, I ended up in Melbourne, Australia, to take up a job in the emergency department at St Vincent's Hospital. Perhaps not as far as the sea could take me, but close enough. I felt homesick almost immediately, and the confronting strength and clarity of that feeling disturbed me. I experienced a huge, gaping emptiness, a longing, which could rise up and overwhelm me at any time. I was homesick without having a place that felt like home.

In time, I settled down, found a house and made friends. I could hide from my grief but never entirely escape it. It was always there, an unsettling presence in the background.

I vividly recall a particular night shift. It was that time, around 5am, when cortisol levels drop, and you shiver as every fibre of your body tells you that you should be asleep. Time becomes flexible. Speeding up for the adrenaline-charged emergencies, slowing down for the routine cases.

I had taken a quick break to fuel myself with caffeine and carbohydrates. The nurses had dimmed the lights in the department.

It was as quiet as an emergency department can ever be. The beep of monitors or the rattle of trolleys occasionally broke the silence.

Working on autopilot, I dragged myself into another cubicle where an elderly man was chatting to his wife in Italian. As I introduced myself, they turned and looked at me in astonishment.

I was about to ask if they would like me to find an interpreter when the man turned to his wife and said with excitement, 'Did you hear, did you hear? She's got my accent.'

His was unmistakably a North Antrim accent. I was about to ask him where he was from, but he was talking, excited now, eager to tell me his story.

'Oh, they were great lads,' he said. 'Great craic.' As he said this, I smiled at the sheer Northern Irishness of that word.

'I came to Australia from Italy when I was a young man. Italy was a bad place to be then, so I came here and got a job cutting sugar cane. I didn't speak any English and I was so unhappy. I was lonely, homesick. I didn't want to stay, but I couldn't go home.

'Then, one day, I met this group of Irish lads,' he said smiling, 'and they took me in. They taught me English and after that ...' He paused for a moment, and then continued, 'Everything was better. I had friends, and what a time we had. Then I met my wife!' He looked at her and smiled.

'Oh, they were great lads,' he said. 'Great craic.'

As he said this, I smiled at the sheer Northern Irishness of that word. Did he realise that he was still carrying a part of those boys around with him? They had become part of him.

'Often, when I speak English, people laugh and say, "Why do you speak English with such a funny accent?" 'But I don't care,' he laughed, 'it reminds me of those boys and how much I loved them'.

'I think it's a lovely accent,' said his wife, taking his hand and smiling at him as if she was recalling the moment they fell in love.

'But', said her husband, 'I have never heard anyone else speak with this accent until you came into the room tonight.

'So, tell me, where does my accent come from?'

'Northern Ireland,' I said, 'North Antrim.'

For a moment, neither of us said anything. Then he thanked me for telling him where his accent was from, and I thanked him for reminding me of where I was from - for reminding me of home. As I said this, I had a sudden image of a grey morning and my father in the garden waving to my mother in the kitchen. I remembered the feeling of damp air and

> **"**
> Emergency departments are alive with stories, ours, and our patients'. When the razzle-dazzle and the adrenaline subside, the stories remain.

the smell of smoke mixed with the salt from the sea. As I did, I could feel myself start to cry and I turned away so the man and his wife couldn't see me. When I turned back, he was still smiling at me in delight.

I could not stop thinking about the man as I walked home after my shift. It was a sunny Melbourne morning and the old men on the allotment at the top of Gore Street waved to me as I went past. The air smelled of hot tarmac, freshly watered plants, and damp earth.

When I got home, everyone else was still sound asleep, except for the cat. So, the cat and I went out into our garden, and there I let myself cry properly. Proper crying, not in a polite way but loudly, with great sobs that made my nose run and left me gasping for breath. After about five minutes the tears stopped, and I went to bed exhausted.

In that moment, I understood that it is better to learn to live with the pain of loss, than lock it away. By forcing myself to forget, I had ultimately lost more, lost a part of myself. I may have numbed the pain, but at a price that was not worth paying. Over time it has become easier to bear, like a scar that only throbs now and then.

Though it was more than 20 years ago, I still think of that man. Whether it was from him, the exhaustion that comes at the end of a night shift, or a combination of the two, I felt as though I had been given a gift. The story had connected me to where I was from and my past. It became part of my identity and has remained with me.

Following that encounter, I developed a pride in my accent that I never had before. I felt a power in my voice and how it expressed my narrative.

We all carry our stories with us - concealed under the surface. They lie there, scratching and scraping at the brittle shell we use to cover them up.

Emergency departments are alive with stories, ours, and our patients'. When the razzle-dazzle and the adrenaline subside, the stories remain. Some are painful, some tender. Others are funny. And some we don't forget. We keep them with us, mixed up with our own stories until they become our stories too. They help us make sense of things and remind us of what it is to be human, and all the rewards and loss that entails.

That is what emergency medicine is for me. •

An ambulance responds to an emergency call in the United Kingdom.

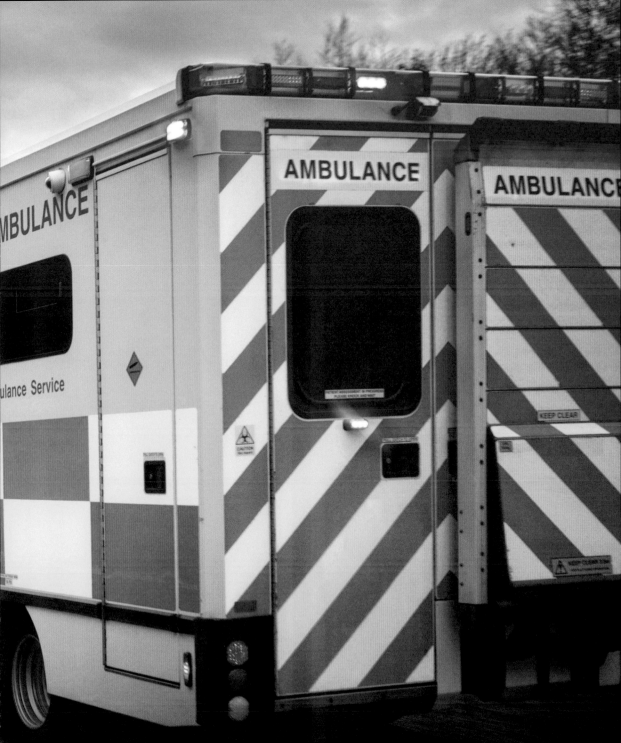

Central Australia from above.

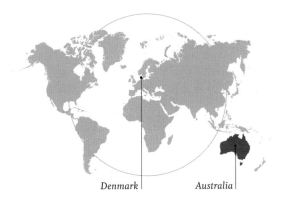

Denmark | *Australia* |

The beating heart of a small town

PETRA NICLASEN AND INA SCHAPIRO

Petra Niclasen is an emergency and retrieval physician in Alice Springs in Central Australia. She grew up in Melbourne, Victoria.

Danish-born Ina Schapiro is an emergency physician at Alice Springs Hospital. She has also worked in Adelaide, South Australia as an emergency medicine trainee and consultant.

Everyone knows everyone else in a small outback town. It's a gift and a curse at the same time.

Petra: There's barely a breeze tonight, so the sound of the phone ringing startles me. It's Gary. He's the husband of my friend and colleague, Ina. He's also an ex-army medic and a keen mountain bike rider.

'Hey, this guy I am mountain biking with has had a medical episode and the ambulance doesn't know how to get to him - we are on the mountain bike tracks behind the scout hall.'

My flatmate is a police officer and overhears the phone call. 'I know where that is. Let's go.' We grab a few items and get ready to head off.

The phone rings again: 'We've started CPR'.

The situation sounds much more serious all of a sudden. But I can't help thinking that it's probably just a faint or a seizure and will all be sorted by the time we get there.

We jump in the four-wheel-drive and my flatmate hurriedly dials her local police colleagues at the station. 'We need someone with an AED (an Automatic External Defibrillator) – and a motorbike.' As the tension increases in the car, she tells me to drive through red lights, with caution.

We hear the phone ping. Gary has sent us a link to Google Maps, with a pin drop at the location of the incident.

When we arrive at the scout hall, we find two police crews and two ambulances, but no-one knows the patient's location. I show them the pin drop and am ushered into a police car with a local officer – he knows the tracks. We navigate using the map on my phone. Lights and sirens.

A lone mountain biker waves us down: 'He's over here'. I jump out and trot through the bush. A policeman is quicker and charges past me carrying the AED. I round some bushes and the scene hits me: a young man, grey in complexion. I have seen this colour before, and it is not compatible with life.

I notice that a work colleague and some friends are gathered around him. CPR is in progress. No-one is smiling. He is not OK.

The patient's name is Robert. He's 34. He collapsed suddenly, cause unclear.

The police officer has the AED open: 'Here Doc, you know how to use this better than me.' I feign confidence as my

> **I feel completely safe – he has skills born of much practice. The whole situation is a little surreal – normally I would love a high-speed ride, but that feels wrong in this case.**

inner voice peeps: 'Err no, not seen this sort before. Shut up. Not helpful. People are looking to me, better read where the pads go.' I try to peel the pads apart and a little bit curls back on itself. I try to unstick it. The inner voice is getting louder: 'Stop stuffing around and slap them on'.

My internal monologue is interrupted by the robotic commands of the AED: 'Assessing rhythm – shock advised'. I push the button, we do a cycle of CPR, and then deliver another shock.

I realise that the ambulance has arrived. The paramedics are the experts in pre-hospital scene management – what are my responsibilities here? Somehow, we all work together without really allocating roles. The police perform excellent CPR and give Robert's friends a rest. Before long, a breathing tube is inserted, and amiodarone – a powerful drug that can correct abnormal heart rhythms – is administered. The monitor shows a non-shockable rhythm.

I am now at Robert's head, breathing for him using an inflatable bag filled with oxygen. The paramedics have recently been trained in the use

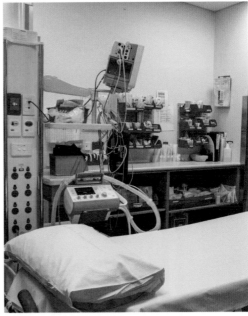

ABOVE LEFT: Alice Springs Hospital.

ABOVE RIGHT: An emergency department resuscitation bay prepared for an incoming patient.

of an automated CPR device. The machine is attached, and Robert is carried 25 metres to the waiting ambulance.

I jump back in with the police officer, who is now escorting the ambulance. Lights and sirens again. He is weaving through traffic, but I feel completely safe – he has skills born of much practice. The whole situation is a little surreal – normally I would love a high-speed ride, but that feels wrong in this case.

Ina, whose husband Gary made the original phone call, happens to be the emergency consultant on shift tonight in the only hospital in town. She is ready to receive the patient alongside a broader team of clinicians. We arrive at the hospital, and I help ventilate the patient as we walk into the emergency department resuscitation bay.

I finally get a chance to speak with Gary and get more of the story. A group of mountain bike riders, including Robert, saw him arrive home from work and asked him to come on their ride. During the ride, Robert had fallen behind. When he caught up, he reported a problem with his bike. While Gary was looking at it, Robert collapsed backwards. Luckily, his fall was broken by the helmet and backpack he was wearing.

The riding group included a doctor, and as soon as Robert's cardiac

Alice Springs in Australia's
Northern Territory.

arrest was recognised, they immediately commenced CPR. But it took another 30 minutes before the AED arrived and the first shock was delivered.

It took 1 hour and 43 minutes from the time of the first phone call I received to arrive at the emergency department.

Ina: I have just rushed off the emergency department floor to eat my dinner when the text appears: 'It is NOT me. A guy on our ride has had a seizure. Petra is here and a team of ambos and police.'

Oh well. It is a small town so I will see the 'guy' when he arrives – he should have stopped seizing by then. I begin to wonder though who the patient is. We've only just moved here, so Gary doesn't know a lot of people. Who has he been riding with? And why is Petra there?

My phone rings. This time it is Petra's flatmate. She explains that they have driven out to the mountain bike trails to help with the situation. It's not a seizure – but a cardiac arrest. In a young, healthy man. They are getting him ready for transport and will be in the emergency department shortly.

> **" For a moment time stops. I know both of these women. They are my neighbours. In this small community, we do not only work together – we practically live together.**

Suddenly my perception changes. I rush downstairs to inform the staff and prepare the resuscitation area. The word is out: 'someone' is being transported in and they are critically unwell. The knowledge stems from an inpatient consultant who has arrived in the emergency department – not in a professional capacity, but to support Robert's fiance, who is also here. She too happens to work in the hospital.

For a moment time stops. I know both of these women. They are my neighbours. In this small community, we do not only work together – we practically live together. Time starts ticking again and I feel my heart beating faster. The stakes have intensified, and my ability to keep my emotions at bay is even more important.

Everyone feels the tension. The preparations for resuscitation proceed smoothly and rapidly. We all sense the urgency.

Then the waiting starts. It feels like an awfully long time has passed since the initial notification. Thoughts fill the void. What could have caused the collapse? A heart attack? A pulmonary embolism - a blood clot that has migrated to his lung? Could it be a snake bite? Possibly.

The seconds and minutes pass. It is close to two hours since the collapse. An inner voice pipes up: 'Well, should we really keep persisting when he gets here? Two hours! If he survives, he will be severely disabled.' Another voice: 'Stop it! He is young, healthy and I am sure he had really effective CPR. It just HAS to go well.'

After 40 minutes my phone rings again. Petra tells me they are five minutes away. Robert briefly regained a pulse but has deteriorated again and is now receiving mechanical compressions.

Finally, the doors swing open from the ambulance bay. The thumping sounds reaches us before we see the trolley. Robert is pale - utterly pale.

From then on everything happens quickly and concurrently: he is transferred across to the bed, his breathing tube is checked, handover takes place, monitors are connected, the defibrillator is readied. There are so many hands, ears, eyes - yet it is quiet but for the constant thumping of the mechanical compressions and the blood pumping in my ears. In a minute I will have to make that decision. We will have to stop the resuscitation, won't we? The situation is surely irreversible.

'Rhythm check,' I say. The thumping stops. My eyes widen - the monitor shows a perfusing rhythm, one compatible with life. Charge dumped. Pulse check: 'There is a pulse'.

> There are so many hands, ears, eyes – yet it is quiet but for the constant thumping of the mechanical compressions and the blood pumping in my ears.

I blink. Did I really hear that? Within seconds, infusions are started, investigations are performed, priorities are shared. The intensive care consultant moves next to me and we make a plan for the next steps in Robert's management. The monitor shows that everything has stabilised.

As we walk towards the lift from the CT scanner, I remain puzzled by what has happened out on that trail - we still have no answers. We exit the lift and I note that Robert's blood pressure is decreasing. Shortly after arrival in the intensive care unit, the rhythm on the monitor suddenly changes into a disorganised and frightening pattern. 'Give a shock,' I yell, realising that we are back to the beginning again. The next 10 minutes are characterised by recurring periods of cardiac arrest and recovery.

I stay and help for another half an hour. It is late and hands are limited.

I marvel over how my team has performed in the meantime – everyone has stayed, everyone has continued working hard, everyone has done a little bit extra.

However, they are also limited in the emergency department, and I have to get back. Other patients requiring urgent care have turned up and we need to get the night staff ready for their shift. I marvel over how my team has performed in the meantime – everyone has stayed, everyone has continued working hard, everyone has done a little bit extra.

I get home after midnight to a distraught husband. He describes what happened on the trails, and how they responded. He also shares the fear, grief and despair that he is experiencing.

The next morning, we hear that Robert arrested again and again overnight. His organs are failing, and everything is looking bleak. The following days are spent at Robert's bedside, with his fiance and family. We also spend time with the other people involved in looking after him that night. Waiting. And hoping.

Days later, Gary and I receive a message: 'He is awake. He is sitting up and talking.' We look at one another – not believing the words in front of us. Respecting family privacy on that special day, we anxiously wait for them to let us know we can visit.

Tears well up in my eyes when I first see Robert, awake, through the glass door. Unsurprisingly, he doesn't recognise us – he has a lot of medication in his system and is experiencing short-term memory loss. However, he is there: smiling, looking very alive, and, unbelievably, sharing his sense of humour with all those at the bedside.

Petra and Ina: The connections you make in a small town can be lifesaving. Robert's story reflects how communities can work together and demonstrate resourcefulness, even in the most challenging of circumstances.

It is difficult to explain the emotions, reactions and reflections that followed in the weeks and months after that night. We still have no answers as to why Robert collapsed. But there is no doubt that the actions of bystanders, friends and colleagues involved in his care – combined with some good fortune – helped save his life.

When we tell people what we do for a living, they often assume that we save lives every day. That's not really the case. Sometimes, just sometimes, however, you get to be a link in a chain of events that is truly extraordinary. And help restore a beating heart in a small town. ●

Sunset over Khartoum, Sudan.

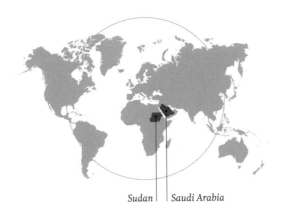

Sudan | Saudi Arabia

Sudanese women and their culture

NADA HASSAN AHMED ABDELRAHMAN

Nada Hassan Ahmed Abdelrahman is an acute care physician and pioneer in the field of emergency medicine in Sudan. She is currently an associate professor at AlMaarefa University in Saudi Arabia.

This is a series of stories that reflect the difficulties and challenges faced by African–Sudanese women. Each case study offers a glimpse of the ways in which a culture that blames women can adversely affect their lives. The stories also illustrate the breadth of experience we have gained in emergency care in the last two decades. Some stories reflect unwise decisions or inadequate setup, but each vividly depicts the arena in which those decisions and interventions are made. These are 'the white-hot moments' within a resuscitation bay where nothing is spared to save a life.

The woman with drenching sweats and tachycardia
The room C medical officer was shouting: 'Her heart rate is 180! I need to put her on the monitor and do an urgent ECG.' A 23-year-old woman was rushed into room A. She had sinus tachycardia with a few atrial ectopics and was sweating from head to toe. We knew only that she had been

brought in by a driver after collapsing on a local bus. Our five emergency beds were occupied, so we had to temporarily borrow a monitor from an 85-year-old man recovering from a massive stroke. Immediate resuscitation was started - we inserted two large-bore cannulas and gave a bolus of fluid.

The medical officer rushed a glucose sample to the lab and returned a few minutes later, shouting: 'Hypoglycaemia, hypoglycaemia! Give her dextrose.' We immediately initiated our hypoglycaemia protocol and, within an hour, our patient had fully recovered.

Later, as I sat beside this young woman's beside and enquired about her history, I learned that she did not have diabetes but, instead, was eating up to eight meals a day to gain weight in the lead-up to her imminent marriage ceremony. She said she was often hungry and that her family fed her frequently and was encouraging her to put on weight. When I asked a standard question about her current medication, she became evasive and denied taking anything. I asked to see her thigh and found severe needle marks. First, she asked me not to tell her family. Then she confessed that, on the advice of her friends, she had started to take insulin injections about a month ago to help her to put on weight. She admitted that she had taken an injection earlier that day and had been busy and not eaten - and that's how hypoglycaemia had landed her in the emergency department.

> The literacy rate among women in Sudan is very low, and most girls leave school to marry early. These young, uneducated girls yearn to be our society's vision of beautiful.

Next, I sat with this young woman's mother and told her about the situation and informed her of the adverse consequences of taking insulin with no indication. She eventually understood that her daughter's actions could mean death. We agreed that the mother should talk to her daughter gently and keep a close eye on her in the lead-up to her wedding, and in the future. My colleagues and I determined that in future cases we would opt to inform a close family member as we had done this time or, where that was not possible, call in a social worker.

Obesity is a sign of beauty in our society and skinny girls are abundant. Men prefer to marry obese women. We see many forms of insulin injections taken by young girls to increase their appetite and put on weight. I cared for another young patient a few months earlier who ended up with steroid-induced mediastinitis after taking 6mg dexamethasone tablets three times a day to put on weight.

The literacy rate among women in Sudan is very low, and most girls leave school to marry early. These young, uneducated girls yearn to be our society's vision of beautiful. They desire obesity, at any cost—even if it jeopardises their lives.

The woman with abdominal pain and shock

The 28-year-old woman in Room C was suffering severe lower abdominal pain and nausea, and said she had been vomiting for more than an hour. She said that her last meal was eggs and suggested this might be the cause of her abdominal symptoms. She did not have diarrhoea and said she was menstruating. As I took her history, she started sweating and her hands became cold and clammy. I rechecked her vitals and found that her blood pressure had dropped. Immediate fluid resuscitation was started and, upon quick assessment, I discovered that her conjunctiva were getting paler. Immediately, I thought that this might be an ectopic pregnancy, yet my patient insisted that she was single, and a virgin.

In our emergency department, taking a urine sample for a pregnancy test requires patient consent and is not available as a routine investigation. The sample must be sent to a private laboratory. To tell an unmarried patient that she might be pregnant, and that a test is needed for confirmation, can be fraught with danger. In an Islamic male-centred culture, the social stigma can put a patient's life at risk. Fortunately, we had an old ultrasound machine. I performed a bedside abdomen scan, which reavealed free fluid. I immediately called for an urgent obstetrical consultation. A young consultant rushed to us and confirmed my suspicions and the surgical team agreed to operate. The patient was transferred to the operating theatre and her family was notified that she had an abdominal pain that required emergency intervention. They trusted our wisdom and allowed us to operate.

In a conservative Muslim society, illegal pregnancies are considered a crime. Our patient could have been sent to jail or, worse, killed or even buried alive by her family to hide their shame. Our 'official' diagnosis and subsequent treatment undoubtedly saved her life.

The woman with hysteria

The young woman in our emergency department shouted and kicked at everything in her path. She had been brought in by her family and rejected all help and all attempts to take her vital signs. A junior doctor ordered the nurses to give her diazepam to calm her down. But unfortunately, the doctor did not take a thorough history from her family. The 23-year-old woman was treated on the assumption that her aggression was a case of 'hysteria'. Diazepam is often used as a drug to calm patients with hysteria, but in this young woman's case, it was lethal and caused immediate central respiratory depression. Unbeknown to the team, she was already suffering from hypoxia (low oxygen in the blood) due to extensive pulmonary tuberculosis.

The young patient collapsed, stopped breathing and was rushed to the resuscitation rom. We immediately began CPR, but all our attempts failed. Just minutes later, her brother, rushed in and handed me her referral letter. Devastatingly, it revealed a known case of extensive bilateral tuberculosis. The referral letter, written in English and not understood the by the family, had recommended an urgent hospital transfer due to very low oxygen levels.

This young woman's needless, tragic death was caused because her hypoxia was wrongly diagnosed on arrival as a 'hysterical conversion'. This is a diagnosis that our society frequently and wrongly attributes to women, merely on the basis of their gender. Too often, the health problems of women of all ages are belittled or dismissed and they are described simply as hysterical.

Sudanese women in poorer areas at the outskirts of Khartoum are usually oppressed. Many marry an unknown, older husband at an early age, or are prevented from going to school by their fathers or brothers at primary grades. Their psychosocial problems are core issues, and they are unable to express their feelings of rejecting their husbands. Their only resort is to pretend that they are having a psychological breakdown, become aggressive, shout, and become 'hysterical'.

Many are taken to local healers, and only in extreme cases will their families take them to hospital. Young girls are subjected to female genital mutilation, which has many consequences including difficult labour, repeated UTI, infected vulval cysts or severe complications, such as massive bleeding and shock. Such cases are becoming rarer, but still some tribes will not allow husbands or family members to donate blood, even if a woman is dying. In Sudan, only relatives are permitted to donate blood.

> **"**
> Too often, the health problems of women of all ages are belittled or dismissed and they are described simply as hysterical.

The woman who lost consciousness

One morning, as I began my shift, I walked into the resuscitation room and found a medical officer writing a death certificate. When I asked him what the cause of the death was, he replied that he didn't know. The patient was a 35-year-old woman from South Sudan, who had been delivered to the emergency department in an unconscious state. Her vitals were not recorded on her file during her initial admission and her family (her husband, his mother, and his second wife) said she had developed sudden extreme shortness of breath and lapsed into a coma. Instinctively, I knew that the case warranted further investigation.

When I questioned her family members, they became aggressive and demanded they be given the woman's death certificate so they could bury her quickly. I could see no tears in their eyes. Their eyes were hard and cold. This case occurred before 2011, during the separation of North and

South Sudan and the family saw the political situation as an opportunity to provoke an argument and deny me a chance to investigate what had caused her death. They started shouting at me, 'Because we are from South Sudan and you from North Sudan, you intend to delay us'.

My worst suspicions were confirmed as I went over to inspect the woman's body. Her dark skin concealed many immediate signs, but a closer look at her neck revealed a fine line of ulcerated skin. It was possible that she had been strangled. Immediately, I notified the police officer and ordered an urgent post-mortem. Unsurprisingly, this was not well received by her family, and they threatened to kill me; I had to escape through a side door.

A post-mortem investigation found that her husband and his second wife had strangled her. They later confessed that they wanted to take her baby away, because the second wife had been unable to conceive.

I sometimes wonder whether emergency physicians should be considered the 'Sherlock Holmes' of the medical profession. We deal with so many bizarre and tragic cases. Sometimes we are the only advocates for our patients – during their lives and even after their deaths.

> We deal with so many bizarre and tragic cases. Sometimes we are the only advocates for our patients – during their lives and even after their deaths.

The malingering woman

A 32-year-old woman presented in our emergency clinic with severe left-sided abdominal pain, distension, and constipation. The onset of her abdominal pain had started two years earlier after she had needed an emergency splenectomy – an operation to remove her spleen – following a road accident. Since then, she had been to multiple clinics in the local countryside and the doctors who examined her had been unable to find any cause for her symptoms. Local healers had prescribed herbs without any improvement. In desperation, her family had taken her to a local healer who was considered an expert in dealing with psychiatric cases. We later learned that she had been at the clinic for more than a month and that the healer had starved, cauterised and beaten her with a whip, claiming supernatural powers were controlling her. This kind of thing occurs often among Sudanese living on the outskirts of Khartoum. Their relatives do not advocate for them or seek investigation and so the healers continue their practice.

"

An abdominal x-ray revealed the core of her sufferings
– a pair of surgical scissors, about 15 centimetres long,
had been left inside her abdominal cavity during an
operation two years ago.

Our clinical examination revealed signs of intestinal obstruction, which we thought might be related to adhesions from her previous surgery. But shockingly, an abdominal x-ray revealed the source of her suffering – a pair of surgical scissors, about 15 centimetres long, had been left inside her abdominal cavity during an operation two years ago. The woman's family explained that her operation had been an emergency procedure in a remote countryside hospital near their home. The family remembered that there had been multiple electrical power blackouts on the day of her operation and the surgeons had completed it with the aid of a mobile phone.

Emergency service in remote areas is highly challenging and doctors work in very stressful situations. If they refuse to work in these poor settings, they know emergency patients might lose their lives. So they make do with limited resources, inadequate equipment, and even mobile phones when there is no electricity. The quality of care declined dramatically around 10 years ago when the government no longer covered the cost of emergency care for the first 24 hours. Now emergency services must be paid for in any public hospital; you die if you do not have money, or your family will not pay.

These stories remind me of three critical aspects of clinical practice in emergency medicine. Firstly, always listen to the patient, especially when things don't add up. Secondly, always complete a thorough physical examination; there may be clues that will lead you to an early diagnosis. Thirdly, always trust your clinical instinct. It is an important and powerful tool.

More importantly, these stories also remind us that gender discrimination can have drastic and devasting consequences for women's health. As patient advocates, we need to raise awareness within our communities, particularly about the life-threatening behaviours and cultural practices that endanger the lives of women in our society. •

An aerial view of
Funafuti atoll in Tuvalu.

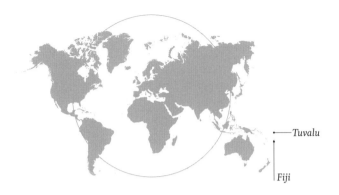

Tuvalu

Fiji

Catching waves beyond the horizon

ALOIMA TAUFILO

Aloima Taufilo is the first doctor from Tuvalu to undertake specialist training in emergency medicine. Normally based at the Princess Margaret Hospital in Funafuti, she is currently living in Suva, Fiji, while completing a Master of Medicine through Fiji National University.

O h no! What have I gotten myself into?
I closed my eyes and quickly sent up a silent prayer. 'Please protect me, I want to see my family again!'
As the waves lashed against the side of the boat, and my life flashed before my eyes, I was taken back to the relative calm of that morning. It seemed like such a long time ago …

The beginning
I was awoken by the sound of a nearby rooster, crowing at the crack of dawn. With each crow, the sun inched a little higher in the sky. I decided to lay a bit longer, cherishing the peace and quiet, but it was short lived.

I heard someone tiptoe into the room. 'Mommy, can I stay home today? I don't feel like going to school.' I turned to see Mister 6, my son, standing at the foot of our bed with his eyes wide open.

'Good morning sonny boy', I whispered back as he crept towards me.

I hugged him and said, 'How about we make a deal? You go to school today and in the afternoon when Mom and Dad get back from work, we will all go for a *launi* (cruise) on the motorbike and get ice-cream. How's that sound?'

Before I could finish my sentence, the words *launi* and ice-cream were enough to make him grin from ear to ear. He was jumping up and down, beaming with joy, waking his dad in the process.

'Daddy, wake up! I want to go to school! Daddy hurry, we're going for a *launi* and ice-cream after school.'

'So much for a peaceful morning in bed', I thought to myself.

Our morning routine revolved around Mister 6. The only difference was that today was *togiga* (matching outfits) day. Our Ministry for Health's *togiga* is a white t-shirt, paired with a purple sulu (wraparound skirt) and a head garland made from sweet-smelling natural flowers – the island scent. I needed to prepare my outfit.

'Today will be a good day,' I thought to myself as I entered the hospital and noticed the empty waiting area in front of the outpatient department.

As I packed lunch for my son, I ran through my commitments for the day. I had an important meeting with our director for health; then I would need to do my morning rounds of admitted patients; then attend the outpatient department; then coordinate simulation training for our newly appointed triage nurses … Oh! I almost forgot; I would also need to do some grocery shopping for the *fakaala* (island feast) tonight.

'Earth to my wife', muttered hubby. His comment broke my train of thought, and I turned to see my man waiting for a response.

Apologetically, I muttered back, 'Sorry hon, what were you saying?'

'I was asking if you want to have lunch at the food stall near the bank?'

'Oh yeah! Sure, let's have lunch there. I'll meet you at 1pm', I answered.

And just like that, we were all ready to go. Turning on the ignition of my motorbike, Mister 6 and I waved our goodbyes and went on our way.

First stop, drop my son to his classroom. Second stop, my workplace, Princess Margaret Hospital – the only tertiary hospital in the country, with 50 beds and healthcare responsibilities for approximately 12,000 people.

'Today will be a good day', I thought to myself as I entered the hospital and noticed the empty waiting area in front of the outpatient department.

'Morning Doc, a phone call for you. From the police station', Nurse Noa said as she handed me the phone. It was 7:55am.

ABOVE: Motorbikes traverse a coastal road in Tuvalu.

'Please let it not be another drunkard. It's too early. The weekend has not even started', I thought.

'*Talofa*, Dr Alo here, how can I help you?' As I spoke into the phone, I could hear a lot of noise in the background.

'Doc, we received a distress call from a nurse on one of the islands in the north. Her calls could not get through to the hospital's line, so she contacted us via our radio transmitter system. It sounds really urgent, and she needs to speak to a doctor as soon as possible.' I could hear the trembling voice of the police officer from the other end of the line, as he tried to relay the message.

'Thanks officer for calling us. I'll be there in a few minutes.'

So much for a good day.

Hurriedly, I got onto my bike again and headed towards the police station, taking the quieter seaside route.

'It's been so dusty and dry lately. I hope it will rain soon', I thought. 'Oh, that reminds me, our water tank needs a refill. I wonder how long our current water supply will last. I guess I'll have to postpone the washing this weekend until we get rain.' It had been three months since the last downfall …

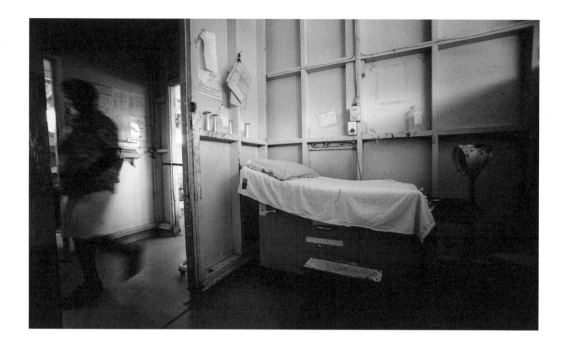

'Morning Doc, the staff nurse is on the line, waiting for you', the police officer said as he led me into their communications room.

ABOVE: A maternity assessment bed in a remote facility in the Pacific.

The situation

Staff nurse Lily had been struggling overnight with a complicated obstetric case. Her patient was a woman with diabetes, 38 weeks, prolonged labour, footling breach presentation with possible fetal distress. This was enough information to get my adrenaline pumping as I hurried back to the hospital to inform our obstetrician.

There are usually two nurses staffing the health clinics in each of our outer islands. The healthcare they can deliver is limited to the available resources. More complex medical conditions - those that require imaging, laboratory investigations or surgical interventions - are referred to the only hospital in the country, on the capital island. Emergency evacuation from this particular island would take 48 hours by sea, 24 hours each way. Unfortunately, this is the only route to retrieve patients.

A few hours later, Dr Jo, the obstetrician, and I were packed and ready to go. I was to be responsible for the patient's overall care during transfer, and Dr Jo would focus on her obstetric management. We were to travel there on

The Voyager, which would depart from the port in Funafuti.

Luck had it that there was a small fishing vessel on the island, which would be heading back to the capital. After some careful planning involving the Ministry of Communication and Transport, it was agreed that the patient would be loaded onto the fishing vessel and *The Voyager* would rendezvous with it halfway. This would save us at least 24 hours.

Dr Jo and I boarded the vessel, and it left the port almost immediately. After an early dinner with the ship's captain and his crew, we went straight to our rooms. *The Voyager* had begun to sway, and I already felt lightheaded and nauseous.

'Hope I feel a bit better when I wake up', I thought to myself.

I had a good nap and was awoken by a knock on the door. I could feel the ship swaying aggressively. I struggled to stabilise myself when I tried to stand.

'How long was I out for?', I asked the crew member who came to wake me.

'Oh! Both of you were out for 11 hours. But the captain told me to come and wake you because we've reached our destination. The fishing vessel is just up ahead', he explained as we made our way to the bridge.

As we emerged onto the top deck, I could see heavy rain and a large swell out the window. It was pitch black. I checked my watch, and it was 3am.

I had never seen waves as big. And I could not see the other fishing vessel. The only clue to its presence was a red dot on the monitors, positioned to the starboard side of the ship.

I was worried. Heavy rains and large swell are the worst combination for an emergency retrieval. Especially one involving a boat-to-boat transfer in the middle of the night.

'Ah, the irony of it starting to rain now! After such a long dry!' I thought.

The Voyager was too big to come alongside the fishing vessel, so we would need to retrieve the patient by tender. Fear crippled me as I made my way to the 3-metre by 2-metre tin boat that we would use to access the fishing vessel. This was, by far, the scariest moment of my life.

I closed my eyes and quickly sent up a silent prayer. 'Please protect me, I want to see my family again.'

> I closed my eyes and quickly sent up a silent prayer. 'Please protect me, I want to see my family again.'

The transfer

The rough seas and bad weather required us to take extra care when getting on and off the tender. I had to time my jump to avoid being crushed between the small boat and *The Voyager*. In that moment, I think I discovered some extra senses that I never knew existed.

The swell was so big that, at some points, the tender was 3 metres below the deck of *The Voyager*. I watched as the enormous waves lifted it to my level. At the right time, I quickly yet carefully stepped on the edge of the tender, before the ship's crew helped me descend into its tin frame.

The movement of the water was so overpowering that I lost my balance. I intuitively grabbed the edge of the tender, but luckily one of the crew held me steady and quickly pulled my hand away from the side of boat, moments before it slammed against the ship. The action saved my fingers from certain injury.

During our journey towards the small fishing vessel, there was a moment when I could not see the *The Voyager*. Panic overcame me. But as another big wave lifted our boat, I saw the lights from the ship and immediately felt relieved. Our journey took a while – it was slow going – but we eventually arrived at the side of the fishing vessel and boarded it with the help of the fishermen.

As I entered the small cabin, I saw our patient and nurse Lily, looking tired and drained from their long, rough journey. Miraculously, our patient's vital signs had remained within normal limits throughout the trip, but she was still experiencing contractions. Unfortunately, we had no way of knowing the condition of the foetus, so we made the quick and deliberate decision to transfer her back to *The Voyager*. It was safer, sturdier, and would get us back to Funafuti in the shortest possible time.

We did not have a stretcher, so we improvised with a mat. With the help of six crew members, we gently lifted the patient, all the while trying not to lose balance. The heavy rain had made the floor of the fishing vessel slippery.

It was a precarious operation. Every crew member worked to lift the patient. They held on tightly to one another, or a rope, the vessel, a side window – anything. As we reached the edge of the fishing vessel, the six crew members paused to allow the tender to rise to the same level, before simultaneously stepping in. With the help of three other crew members, who were already on board, they managed to support and lift the patient into the tender.

Wave after wave, the tender rocked back and forth, violently at times. We covered our patient to shield her from the heavy rain and thanked the

> ## In the controlled chaos of emergency medicine, the waves are often crashing around us, sometimes metaphorically, and sometimes quite literally.

captain of the fishing vessel and his team for their help. We waved them goodbye, then began the fraught journey back to the mothership, cursing the weather as we went.

Thankfully, things had settled a little by the time we reached *The Voyager*. The crew hooked the tender onto the ship's crane, and we were lifted to safety. I immediately sent up another silent prayer: 'Thank you for your protection. Please guide us safely back home.'

Back in the relative calm of the ship, I connected the patient to the monitoring equipment while Dr Jo assessed her. For the first time in several hours, I felt as though we were in control of the situation. There was still a long way to go, but we were on our way home.

The ending

Twelve hours later, we reached the mainland and went straight to the hospital. Our patient required further imaging before she headed to the operating theatre. Dr Jo and her team managed the situation diligently and provided the best possible care at all times. It was a harrowing journey for all involved.

I was relieved to be back on solid ground. The opportunity for lunch near the bank, and to attend the *fakaala*, had long since passed, but I didn't mind. I'd had the privilege of caring for a patient in the direst of circumstances, supported by a team of remarkable individuals connected by a common goal.

Emergency doctors can't address every health concern or manage every problem. But we can facilitate care, and make sure that patients receive the right treatment, at the right time, in the right place. It is a privilege to hold such a responsibility.

In the controlled chaos of emergency medicine, the waves are often crashing around us, sometimes metaphorically, and sometimes quite literally. These experiences only make us stronger and more resourceful. They also serve to remind us of the things that really matter.

As I walked into the house, contemplating these thoughts, Mister 6 turned and ran towards me. 'Mommy, we missed you! Where have you been? Guess what happened at school yesterday ...' •

As with many small island nations of the Pacific, climate change poses a direct threat to Tuvalu.

Aerial view of Dar es Salaam in Tanzania.

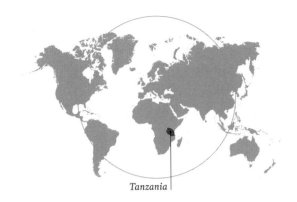

Tanzania

A legacy of hope

ALPHONCE NSABI SIMBILA

Alphonce Nsabi Simbila is an emergency physician in the Emergency Medicine
Department of Muhimbili National Hospital in Dar es Salaam, Tanzania. He also supports
the training of medical students and junior doctors affiliated with Muhimbili University of
Health and Allied Sciences.

O n one normal night at Muhimbili National Hospital, I was the
only senior trainee on a shift that seemed fairly calm. This was
unusual for the 1500-bed national referral facility, where the
emergency medicine department can see and treat patients from all
over the country. Our department supports the senior trainees in their
final year of training to make semi-autonomous decisions on patient
management under the supervision of an attending physician. On this
shift, I had been allocated a supervisory role.

I assigned myself to one of the resuscitation rooms, which usually
receives patients who need ventilatory support. I kept an eye on things
throughout the department, checking on my juniors and the patients they
were caring for. From time to time, the staff popped into my resuscitation
room with questions, asking for advice or reassurance on the management
of their patients.

At around 1am, I walked by resuscitation room three, designated for children aged under 14. Through half-shut curtains, I could see one of my junior colleagues diligently attending to one of four children squeezed into the space. 'Do you need any help with any of the patients in this room?', I asked. 'I am almost done. I have one more patient to see', she replied, quickly pointing to a stretcher close to the door.

I turned to see a little girl lying on her back. I noticed she was staring distractedly at the various cartoon paintings on the ceiling. Beside the stretcher was a young woman on a chair, dozing gently amidst the general hum of the department. I walked over to greet the girl who smiled, greeted me back, told me her name and generally appeared well at first glance. Recognising that the girl might be too young to give me specific details about how she came to be in the emergency department, I woke the woman who was dozing by her side by greeting her loudly.

As a way of establishing rapport, I asked in a friendly manner what brought the girl, aged about 7, to the hospital that night. The young woman sighed, sat up straight, and began her story.

Tumaini, her only child, was a grade two student from one of the regions in southern Tanzania. She was well until a week prior to their arrival at the

The region that Tumaini and her mother were from had neither the imaging nor neurosurgical services that she needed.

emergency department, when she came home from school complaining of back pain, requesting to lie in bed and to 'rest a little bit' because she was not feeling well. Hours passed and dinner was ready, so her mother went to wake her up.

Standing at the door, she called out, but Tumaini did not emerge. She called her again, this time with a tone that meant she was serious, but her daughter still did not come out. Tumaini replied from within the room that she could not get up. Her mother insisted that she stop joking around and come to have dinner quickly; then she could go back to sleep afterwards. Tumaini, with a similar tone, replied she could not get up and needed help to stand. Her mother went in to try to assist her off the bed, but she was floppy and completely unable to support her own weight.

Panic set in and the mother did not know what to do. She hurriedly carried Tumaini to the nearby health facility. She used a traditional piece of cloth called a 'khanga', commonly used as a baby wrap, to secure her daughter tightly against her back.

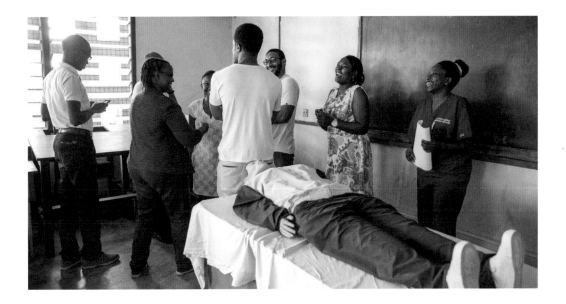

ABOVE: Emergency
medicine physicians
and trainees discuss
cases at Muhimbili
National Hospital.

At the local health facility, they were received by a clinical officer who conducted an initial assessment and performed the few available tests. He suggested either a CT scan or an MRI of the spine and hinted that Tumaini would need a neurosurgical service as well.

The region that Tumaini and her mother were from had neither the imaging nor neurosurgical services that she needed. All that the doctor could do was administer pain medications and refer Tumaini to the national referral hospital for further management.

They had no ambulance at the facility, so Tumaini's mother had to organise transport, which she could not afford. She carried her child back to their home. For a week she went around borrowing money from her fellow workers and friends until she could get a bus fare to the national referral hospital. She travelled more than 14 hours on a bus with Tumaini, who had a suspected spinal injury. Wearily, she disembarked from the bus, then carried her child on her back to reach Muhimbili National Hospital.

I couldn't believe what I was hearing. I looked at the girl lying comfortably on a stretcher, smiling. Without any clear intent, I found myself asking her if she had eaten. Tumaini had a bottle of orange juice on the way. I went on and asked her to move her hands, which she could barely do. 'How about moving your toes and feet?' I asked. 'I can't', she replied. I took a deep breath and instructed her to close her eyes and tell

ABOVE: Emergency physician Upendo George discusses an x-ray with emergency medicine trainees.

me whenever she could feel any sensation in her legs. 'No, I can't feel anything, I don't know why!' she replied softly. 'My friend pushed me hard against a desk and I fell on its corner on my back when we were playing in class. That is how it started,' she explained.

I stood there in disbelief, completely lost for words. I had been practising emergency medicine for a couple of years and had seen many unexpected conditions in patients, but hearing this young girl's story shattered my heart. I collected myself, tried hard to keep my composure, to hide the sadness that was almost taking me to the ground. I excused myself from the room, went into the bathroom, sobbed, washed my face, and called a junior trainee to come and re-examine the child. She examined her and reported the same findings.

After I regained strength, I went into the room to explain to the mother and child what had happened. I had never struggled with explanations to patients the way I did that day.

"

I had been practising emergency medicine for a couple of years and had seen many unexpected conditions in patients, but hearing this young girl's story shattered my heart.

'I believe my daughter will be fine. My daughter and I have come from very far away to seek a cure. She is the only child I have. I am raising her so that she can come and help me in the future', the mother told me, in tears, as I finished explaining the possible outcomes of Tumaini's condition.

I felt empty, helpless. I felt as though I had failed the child. I envisioned this young girl's future ruined by not getting the right emergency service at the time when she needed it the most.

This young girl had suffered a traumatic spinal injury days before presenting to our emergency department. Now, she could neither move nor feel her limbs. I was enduring the psychological and moral pain because I understood the significance and severity of her condition. She might never walk again.

As emergency clinicians, we work at the coalface of medicine, seeing and treating patients every hour of the day, every day of the year. Yet the barriers to accessing that care are real – whether they are geographical, financial, social or cultural.

This little girl represents the many trauma patients from low and middle-income countries who undertake similar arduous journeys and end up with unfavourable health outcomes. Prehospital care is needed globally; it has the potential to reduce morbidity and mortality in our communities.

This child's story is devastating. But it should inspire us to work together to build systems that enable safe and timely treatment for all patients, wherever they are in the world. I hope this becomes Tumaini's legacy. •

ACKNOWLEDGEMENTS
The editorial team acknowledges the premature passing of Muhimbili emergency physician Upendo George, pictured in the images on pages 57 and 58. Upendo was a much loved and highly valued member of the emergency care community in Tanzania. The images from Muhimbili National Hospital that accompany this story were supplied by the Abbott Fund.

Upendo Julius (left) and Australian volunteer Tiffany Tiong (right) weighing Upendo's child to inform the delivery of health services by the Flying Medical Service in Arusha, Tanzania. Tiffany was supported by the Australian Volunteers Program to volunteer as a nurse trainer in 2018.

Rainforest canopy
near Cairns in
Queensland, Australia.

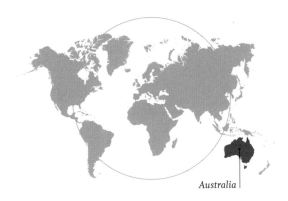

Australia

The power of stories in the emergency department

TILEAH DRAHM-BUTLER

Tileah Drahm-Butler, a social worker and narrative therapist, grew up in Brisbane, Australia. She now lives in Cairns, in Far North Queensland, where she works as an emergency department social worker.

I write from the lands of the Gimuy Walubara Yidinji people. Their stories are embedded in the spirit of this country. Wherever we may be, our personal journeys are lived alongside the first stories of the land. First Nations people have always understood the power of stories, sharing wisdom through narrative since time immemorial.

I am continually inspired by the power of story in my work as an emergency department social worker. I have learned that, in times of crisis and trauma, people can tell their stories in ways that create meaning. This in turn can shape how they heal and go on to live their lives.

The emergency department, with all its busyness, is a frontline of human suffering. Amid the incessant beeping of monitors and the code calls over the paging system, sounds of distress are common. It is a hive of activity, punctuated by the constant movement of staff. Some stories, however, transcend the chaos. Somehow, immersed in stories, I find calm.

Love and concern

There are many stories of love and concern in the department. Some of them are complex. Like that of Jim and Mary, an elderly couple who I met in Cairns Hospital. I could see that care had been taken to get Jim dressed for the day – his well-ironed, checked shirt was tucked into his shorts, and his hair was neatly brushed to the side. Mary was also dressed nicely, but she wore a worried expression.

Jim lived with dementia, and his disease had progressed to a point that meant Mary was no longer able to meet his care needs at home. To facilitate Jim's transition into residential aged care, Mary had been told by a health professional to bring him into the department, but under false pretences. She'd been advised to tell Jim that he had a routine appointment, when the real objective was hospital admission and, at some later stage, transfer to an aged care facility. The intent was to minimise Jim's distress, but the whole situation was profoundly upsetting for Mary.

When Mary relayed this advice, the doctor and I agreed that we could not participate in the fabrication. It did not align with our personal or professional ethics. When we explained this to Mary, she began to cry. They were tears of sadness, but also of relief.

> "
> The realisation was difficult for Jim, and Mary, but she was adamant this was the right approach. Mary told her story as an act of love, and I was honoured to be its witness.

Mary told us that lying to Jim was out of keeping with her principles, but she felt so guilty for 'leaving him' that she'd felt compelled to comply. She was most concerned about giving up on her 'promise' – a vow they had made to look after one another, even through sickness.

'How did you and Jim meet?' I asked Mary. She told us that, in his teenage years, Jim was a hard-working labourer and that, sometimes, at the end of a long working day, he would come to her window. She would sneak out at night to meet him. Mary and Jim went on to marry and raise a family. Their love story had stretched over 60 years. Through the various chapters, I learned how they managed family, work and aspiration. Mary described Jim as her best friend.

I asked Mary what dementia had taken from their relationship. She said that since becoming Jim's carer, her role as his wife and best friend was diminished. Mary hoped to regain this aspect of their relationship when someone else was helping with his care needs. Through the telling of it, Mary was able to breathe life back into their love story. In my time

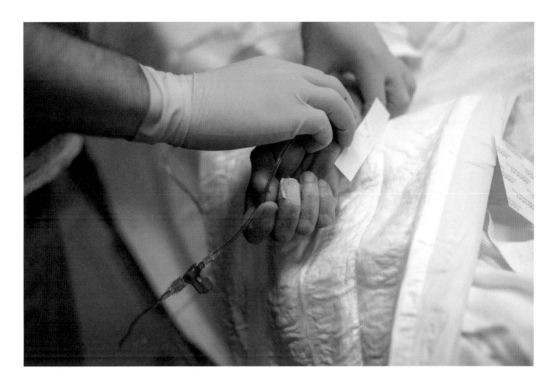

ABOVE: A patient receives care in the emergency department.

with her, she came to realise that facilitating his ongoing care was not betraying their love after all.

When the doctor told Jim what was happening, he began to cry. He said to Mary, 'How could you? You promised.' The realisation was difficult for Jim, and Mary, but she was adamant this was the right approach. Mary told her story as an act of love, and I was honoured to be its witness.

Coming in and coming out

Many of the stories we hear in the emergency department are worthy of celebration. Often, these are stories of change and realisation of one's preferred way of being. When I challenge the heteronormative gaze, I sometimes get to witness and participate in stories of coming out. This was true for Sam, who arrived by ambulance. Sam had been placed under an involuntary treatment act because of concerns they (non-gendered pronoun) were acting in unusual ways, principally by appearing cheerful and nude in public. Some people had interpreted this as evidence of psychosis.

When I meet people in the department, I try to avoid making assumptions or interpreting expressions. Rather, I like to ask what is going on for them. When I asked this question of Sam, I heard a story of coming out and a celebration of identity.

Sam explained that they had lived most of their life being identified as a male, but this was no longer a comfortable fit. Sam told me that as a child, their mother allowed them to dress up in her clothes. In fact, this was celebrated – Sam's mother would often add lipstick to the beautiful outfits that Sam enjoyed. Sam explained that as they got older, they lived as a man as a means of protect themselves from violence and oppression.

"

I learned from Sam that, in the emergency department, we can join people who are celebrating their identity. Through questioning ideas of normality, we can share in stories of hope and joy.

When we met, it was Pride week in Cairns. Through seeing others rejoice and celebrate their gender diversity, Sam felt supported to do the same. Sam said they were dancing in the nude in celebration, because they had decided to come out to themselves and to others.

When it was time for Sam to leave the department, we agreed that a blue hospital gown was far too daggy, especially during Pride week. I offered Sam some clothes:

'Sam, we have four boxes of clothes: one that we call women's pants and skirts, one that we call men's shorts and pants, another that we call women's tops, and another that we call men's shirts. Where would you like me to get your clothes from?'

With an excited smile, Sam replied, 'I'll have a skirt please'.

'And for a top?'

'Oh, just a t-shirt from whichever box … but make sure it goes with the skirt.'

'Oh Sam', I said, 'that goes without saying!'

Sam left looking fantastic, with a smile to match their outfit. I learned from Sam that, in the emergency department, we can join people who are celebrating their identity. Through questioning ideas of normality, we can share in stories of hope and joy.

The emergency department in Cairns, Far North Queensland.

Honouring people

We sometimes meet people for the first time when they are dying. When we listen as loved ones tell their stories, it can help these relatives and friends make meaning of the person's death, even in a busy emergency department, and even when the circumstance of the death is traumatic and unexpected.

We recently met Dean, a middle-aged First Nations man with chronic illness, who had worked a wide range of jobs all over Australia. Dean didn't have children but had a fathering relationship with his niece and nephew and had settled in Cairns to be with them. Most of Dean's family lived down south so, on this night, as Dean was dying, he was accompanied only by his nephew, Shane.

After the emergency department doctor gently told Shane that Dean was dying, we all stood in silence for a moment, as we often do. When the room had cleared, I asked a simple question of Shane: 'Can you tell me a story about Dean?'

Through Shane's words, I learned that Dean held strong values and opinions about social justice, and believed we could all live more peacefully. Shane described Dean's ideas in detail, along with their philosophical underpinnings. I learned that Dean even had 'business' cards made, so that when he shared his ideas with people, they could stay in touch.

'What do you think it might mean to your uncle, that you are sharing these ideas with me tonight, in such detail?' I asked Shane.

'He'd probably be pretty proud', he replied.

I can only hope that Dean, as he lay dying, found comfort in Shane's telling of his story, of the values and principles that he lived by, and knew that these would be his legacy.

New beginnings

Too often in the emergency department we meet women who have experienced violence from their intimate male partners, and we try to help them to safety. Leaving their partners can be the time when they are most at risk, so in my work I try to position these women as the experts in their life. We often don't know what happens when they leave the department but, in this case, I was honoured to hear what a difference our care had made for Heather.

Heather arrived in an ambulance. She told me the story of her relationship with Kelvin, and what it had meant to her in the beginning. Heather grew up under the care of child protection and had longed for a

> **"**
> I invited Heather to use the metaphor of a butterfly, and we talked about an unknown time in the future, when the caterpillar would transform into the chrysalis.

particular notion of family. She thought she found this with Kelvin but, as time went on, his subtle tactics of power and control had turned into physical violence.

I invited Heather to use the metaphor of a butterfly, and we talked about an unknown time in the future, when the caterpillar would transform into the chrysalis, and she might draw on her wisdom to leave Kelvin and move into the unknown. Heather told me in detail what it would be like to be the butterfly, emerging from this change, and how she would live out her life. She told me that she would study and find a nice place of her own to decorate. In this moment, I was hearing Heather's story through a journey metaphor. That night, she went home to Kelvin.

About a year and a half later, Heather was back in the ED, but this time it was because she had twisted her ankle at work. Heather called me over with a smile and said, 'I remember you, we talked about the butterfly!' She said that, about a month after her first hospital visit, Kelvin had hit her and knocked her to the ground when they were at a park. The first thing she saw when she came to was a butterfly – so she stood up and left.

Heather told me how happy she was now. She had enrolled in a business course, as intended, and was already on the lookout for other opportunities. Her future was looking bright.

Listening to others
When I hear stories, I listen for those that reflect people's everyday acts of resistance. The social determinants of health are a reality for all communities and, on every shift, I bear witness to stories that reflect how power and privilege intersect to shape people's lives.

The demands in the emergency department can be overwhelming, but it is important to make time to listen to people's stories, especially when they have been suppressed through oppression. I seek to stand in solidarity with people from the margins, to breathe oxygen into the embers of their stories, and, in doing so, learn about their hopes, dreams and intentions for living. ●

A massive iceberg in the
Southern Ocean, Antarctica.

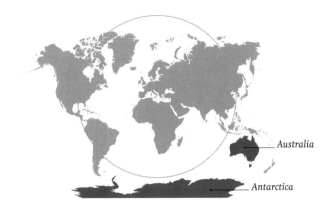

Australia

Antarctica

Reflections from the darkness

MEG McKEOWN

Meg McKeown grew up in Tasmania, worked for 12 years as a veterinarian as her first career out of school and then retrained as a doctor. She did her post-graduate training with the Australian College of Rural and Remote Medicine (ACRRM) in Antarctica and rural Australia.

The dark has changed me.

I spent 12 months in Antarctica with 18 other people. These people were my friends in Australia. We trained together, we laughed as I learned to ride a quad bike for the first time in Hobart and we completed our fire, environment and sea safety training. When we arrived 'on station' in Antarctica, we completed our field training, together. We learned how to achieve a rescue from the field to the medical facility and how to complete a mock anaesthetic and surgical procedure in a slick, well-coordinated operation. We cooked together, played darts, watched movies and threw parties.

Yet, now, I feel alone. I wonder what has happened to them. Or whether it is my perspective that has shifted.

As part of the science program, we are tasked to spend hours each week riding in the Hägglund vehicle trying to spot the first seal haul out. It gives me too much time to think. The sun went down eight weeks ago, and it is still minus 25 degrees celsius. We wear four layers of clothing and carry a survival pack just to get out the door each morning. The ice, covering where the ocean should be, is so thick that we can drive on it in a heavy machine. Occasionally we stop to test its thickness by drilling through it and measuring the depth to the water. We share the job and take it in turns to get cold and miserable as the cold sinks through the layers; we feel as though we will never be warm again. It is always a surprise to see the salt water gush out of the newly drilled hole, even though that is the expected outcome; it's easy to forget that we are driving on frozen ocean. Time bends and the mind wanders as the engine thumps on, everything is hard since the sun went down.

'There is no way that there is a seal out here, no pregnant being would haul out of minus three degrees water to sit on ice at minus 25 degrees', I think to myself. 'If I were pregnant under this ice, I would stay there and refuse to come out to give birth.' My mind wanders, contemplating this idea, but I snap back to the reality in front of me, riding the Hägglund, a remarkable all-terrain amphibious Antarctic vehicle built to triumph over the rough terrains of snow and ice. I must try and stay in the moment; it's hard enough safely completing the dangerous routine tasks. A loss of focus can be fatal.

> I must try and stay in the moment; it's hard enough safely completing the dangerous routine tasks. A loss of focus can be fatal.

This task of the seal census is the riskiest thing we do – just by driving over the ice. The vehicle could plunge through a thin part of the crust at any moment, and we could join the seals in the 'waiting' room. What a rude adventure that would be – for us, and for them. This is also to be avoided for another reason. If we have to radio to the station for assistance, we will owe a whole case of beer to our rescuers. Who has a case of beer left at this end of the season?

No seals again today; sensibly they wait.

I had worked for the Australian Antarctic Division (AAD) for five years before I faced my overwinter on the Antarctic continent. My career has been unique. I trained as a veterinarian in the late 1990s and worked in small animal practice until 2009, when I finished the graduate medicine program at the University of Sydney. I started in the hospital as a trainee and then completed my ACRRM training with the Polar Medicine Unit at the AAD. This role was at sea, meeting asylum seekers in the Indian Ocean as they arrived in Australian waters. I also spent a summer in Antarctica and a year at Macquarie Island in the Subantarctic. I completed my

rural generalist training in general practice in Childers in Queensland, Australia, and I spent a year in Myanmar with the Department of Foreign Affairs and Trade.

All of these roles led me to accept the offer of spending the winter of 2019 at Davis Station in Antarctica. The basics of the role were straightforward, and I thought I was ready. Others who had gone before me tried to counsel me, but nothing prepared me, or could have prepared me, for the experience. Running a medical facility that included a general practice office, procedural room, pathology suite with machines to maintain, surgical theatre with anaesthetic equipment to maintain, a dental suite, x-ray facility, full pharmacy and a ward were the easy parts of the job.

I have changed.

Back at the station I receive a phone call from head office. It is a cheerful person on the end of the phone. This is like a slap in the face. Cheerful isn't something that is in great supply here in the middle of the dark times and often isn't well received by the midwinter expeditioner. 'How are you going?' they ask. I am not sure my frontal lobes are working

> " It is not forever and when the sun does eventually come back up, it will restore most of the disequilibrium.

well when I hear myself say, 'Not great, this darkness is playing havoc with my brain. I don't feel like myself and I would never have volunteered for this had you told me how bad it would get.' I don't have the mental capacity to stop there either. 'It is clearly your fault that I am in this mess. I literally have to take it day by day and nothing is enjoyable, I don't think the sun will ever come up again, I am NEVER coming back here.' I don't remember the response from the other end to this diatribe of vitriol. I no longer had the capacity to care or temper my dismay at my predicament.

I am different.

It is not all negative. I no longer tolerate static. I won't accept a 'can't-do' attitude and I find solutions for adaptive challenges when they are complex or ambiguous. I find solutions for issues that are volatile and unpredictable.

ABOVE: Summer in Antarctica.

The hardest part of my experience was living through the dark and watching myself change. I would get annoyed by the person who left the coffee machine a mess or who failed to make more powdered milk up if they emptied the bucket. One evening I saw a plate with one melting moment on it, covered in cling film with a name written on it next to a plate holding 20 other perfectly good melting moments. I ate that reserved melting moment and, despite there being 20 others, the person who had hoarded that one biscuit in plain sight got quite angry about it. I didn't really care. In my mind it wasn't appropriate to hoard food when we were all in the same boat. But clearly my behaviour was annoying others just as much as their behaviour was annoying me.

Every winter, each Antarctic station has the chance to submit a midwinter short film. Every nation occupying part of the Antarctic territory participates and all films are completed on the same weekend around the continent. The theme is announced on the Friday evening and the teams have until Sunday, two days later, to complete the film. Our station wanted to do a comedy. But I could not face participating in a comedy and convinced everyone that it shouldn't, at least, be slapstick comedy. Most people on station likely thought that would be 'cheering' but I was sure it wouldn't. I got my way, and the film was written. In the final scene, bodies wrapped in garbage bags are burning in a red-hot incinerator. The composition was perfect, and I was very pleased with the outcome. This film was a direct reflection of the impact of the winter on our team.

Two and a half years later I am in private practice in Tasmania working as a rural generalist. I still like meeting the new doctors heading to Antarctica. I don't warn them about the long winter, but I do let them know they can contact me at any time when they are away. Not everyone has the same experience but, occasionally, I do get contacted and can offer reassurance that it is not forever and when the sun does eventually come back up, it will restore most of the disequilibrium.

But the dark has changed me.

I will forever carry that Antarctic winter with me as a difficult time that I made it through, and it is obvious to me now why we refer to hard times as 'dark times'. I am more resilient and my focus on what is important in life is much sharper.

Would I go back? Never say never is the response I give when asked that question. ●

PART 2

CRISIS AND CONFLICT

Reflections on disaster, the pandemic and emergency response

A Palestinian man stands on a street of Gaza city after a night of heavy aerial bombardment.

Rohingya refugee camps in Bangladesh.

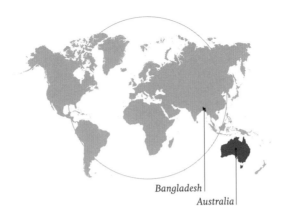

Bangladesh
Australia

Is it right to smile?

EVAN O'NEILL

Evan O'Neill is an emergency medicine consultant based in Australia. He has worked in a variety of contexts with Médecins Sans Frontières, most recently in South Sudan and Bangladesh.

T he first day I visited the emerging refugee camp in Bangladesh we were met by hundreds of people, all crouching in the mud, in the stifling humid air. We had a few boxes, a few people and a few tarpaulins for shade. We were there to provide some therapy but also to assess needs. We could only see a fraction of those waiting and, when we explained this, apologising to the crowd, I saw sad forbearance. At this point, most young men took it upon themselves to leave.

It was August when I first heard of the deadly crackdown on Rohingya Muslims in Myanmar, which had sent hundreds of thousands of Rohingya refugees fleeing into Bangladesh. Now, having been in the district of Cox's Bazaar for two months, I gaze out the window of our Médecins Sans Frontières (MSF) van, headphones in, and sweaty shirt stuck to the seat. We bump and roll away from the clinic, away from the camp and away from our work. The sun yawns with a pink glow as it slumps low behind the hills and lays down today's last rays.

Overseas MSF staff are not allowed in the makeshift settlement after dark. We must leave our colleagues earlier than we would like. From here on, a fickle mobile signal is the only way I can support the doctor who later arrives for night shift. As it is his first time as a solo doctor after hours, we will end up speaking regularly. Later, when the late hours become early, he will help a mother deliver a baby. He will be so proud he won't want to put down the phone.

But all that is yet to come. Right now, I'm still staring out the window. We drive slowly – the only way to safely contend with sleepy cows, distracted pedestrians, speeding buses, lumbering lorries and swarms of tuk-tuks and rickshaws on this narrow rural road. Beyond the crowded shelters of yet another makeshift settlement, a bald knoll catches my eye. It's been denuded of anything green and growing, yet it is alive. A crowd of muddy children fly kites. As they fade into silhouettes, the yellow, pink and green of their kites dance across the drowsy, red dusk. Soon this precious patch of light-brown soil shall surely meet more bamboo and more tarpaulins as Rohinghya refugees continue to arrive.

> At the entry point some race, some stride, some collapse and some are carried. A few are inconsolable, most people stare without any trace of expression.

Our mobile clinic at the entry point tells us about new arrivals; numbers are about 1000 a day. The 'moon boats' with their high keels are picturesque but unstable in the choppy sea, as they carry up to 25 people. Fishing trawlers carry far more. How many perilous journeys cross this channel? And how many wait on the other side? I hear that some people hide in the jungle – scared to move without the support and safety of a significant crowd surrounding them. There would be more arrivals, but some boats tragically capsize, drowning those fleeing the Rakhine State.

From the other side of the van you can see across to the Burmese hills. On some days there are large surges of bilious black smoke below those hills. I read reports of villages razed and hear stories from patients that are even more fearsome.

That channel is gorgeous. Tourists take pictures from atop hills: postcard scenes of high-keeled fishing boats and irrepressible tropical trees lining the shores. That morning the same sunny shore met more refugees. At the entry point some race, some stride, some collapse and some are carried. A few are inconsolable. Most people stare without any trace of expression. We have a mobile clinic at the entry point for those

ABOVE: A staff meeting at an MSF healthcare centre in Cox's Bazar, Bangladesh.

needing immediate medical attention, but most are just assigned to their camp.

From where I sit in the clinic, encounters are short and a line snakes outside under the broiling sun. We need to keep moving, keep registering, keep dispensing, all while keeping a watchful eye on those waiting lest a critical case be sitting, slowly deteriorating. With the help of a translator, the patients are welcomed, their stories listened to, and, after a direct exam, a plan is made and explained. We see the next patient. Details are recorded so that trends can be observed and notes from the encounter are recorded on a small card given to each patient.

The days and the patients inevitably blend, but some are indelibly memorable. I saw an orphan today, 7 months old. The notes belie the extraordinary circumstances. '7 mo M, mild diarrhoea, severe acute

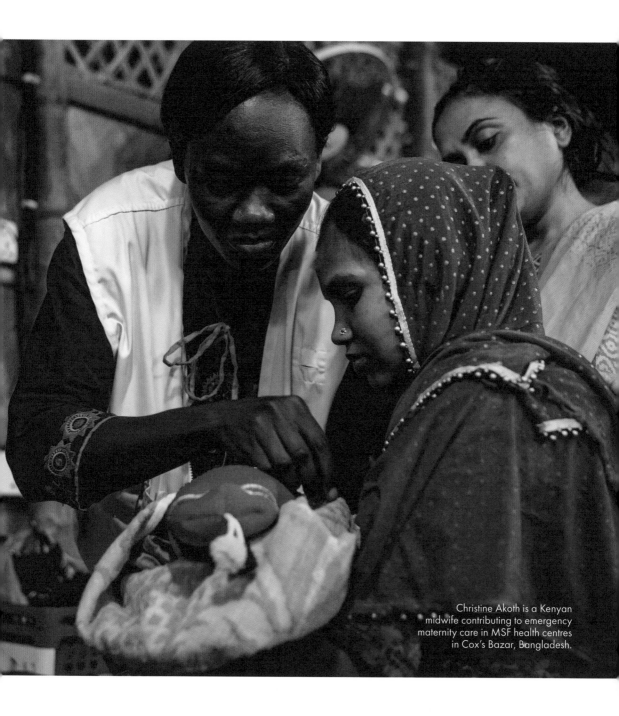

Christine Akoth is a Kenyan midwife contributing to emergency maternity care in MSF health centres in Cox's Bazar, Bangladesh.

malnutrition, stable – referred ambulatory therapeutic feeding centre.'
Adopted and nursed by a kind mother – a mother with four of her own.
They sat waiting in the sun alongside everyone else, Mum in her niqab
with an unknown stranger's child.

Through the translator it was hard to parse events. Essentially the
baby was found alone in Myanmar by someone else, a man. The parents?
Where? Alive? Unknown ... The woman said a man had handed the baby
to her on the crossing of the Naf River. She did not see him again; she talks
while the infant sits softly in the crook of her arm.

This mother has breastfed this feeble baby alongside her own. Her eyes
are heavy and she looks tired, yet she musters a wry smile when greeted.
Without her I'm sure the child would have perished. Her milk has kept
him alive this far, but his severe acute malnutrition (SAM) is obvious from
across the room, the empty folds of skin, the triangular head, the far too
prominent ribs and distant eyes.

> **"**
>
> **The extraordinary events that have led to this
> child being in this mother's arms are told with little
> sentiment, but the arm she wraps around him is no
> less protective.**

She has brought him to the clinic with diarrhoea, common in
malnourished children. The infant's mid upper arm circumference
(MUAC) confirms the diagnosis and, while his big eyes and wasted
appearance are alarming, there is fortunately no sign of complications.
He has not lost his appetite, there is no sign of infection, and he clings
on for cuddles.

The extraordinary events that have led to this child being in this
mother's arms are told with little sentiment, but the arm she wraps around
him is no less protective. He is assessed in her arms, and we speak about
what will happen next.

Some malnourished children are so unwell or fragile that therapeutic
feeding takes place in hospital with close monitoring and treatment
of complications. This bub is not so sick and I'm grateful we have an
Ambulatory Therapeutic Feeding Centre (ATFC) in the next tent. I'm sure
this mother, and this child too, will appreciate their support. Right now, she
just looks exhausted.

Rohingya refugees are among the most vulnerable people in the world and the children are the most exposed. They face malnutrition, trafficking and illness. Some children come to our clinic alone or with their siblings, while their mothers are occupied with all the other children under their tarpaulins.

That was the case for the 10-year-old girl I saw next, with her two-year-old sister in tow. She was worried about her sister's cough. The younger child continued to play, her moist cough punctuating her movements. The cough had been there maybe days, maybe weeks. Her family of seven lived in close quarters on a dirt floor under a tarpaulin roof. Their father was missing. A significant portion of the family's income went to firewood that the Rohingya refugees cut down daily from surrounding forests. Mothers cook indoors on firewood. The smoke affects the children's lungs.

It wasn't clear whether antibiotics would help. Water and some biscuit treats were dispensed. The sister was asked to come back with an adult carer. I didn't see them again. I supposed the toddler must be better, I hoped so anyway.

> **Rohingya refugees are among the most vulnerable people in the world and the children are the most exposed. They face malnutrition, trafficking and illness.**

That morning's walk to the clinic was the same as every other day. Intensely green hills and picturesque rice paddies. We are followed by a flurry of waving arms and high-pitched 'HELLOOOO!'s from smiling local youngsters. Children play in the puddle next to a water pump and a toddler makes a hat out of a discarded melon. Whether it's in sloppy, ankle-deep mud with gumboots or kicking up dry dust in sandals, it's an irrepressibly beautiful way to start any day. I stop at stalls to buy lollies that I can give to children in the clinic. I smile as I walk.

My smile is reliably arrested upon seeing the camp again. Tarpaulin shelters stacked on hills where people proudly battle both the elements and poverty. Is it still right to smile? I don't know. It's reliably unsettling. Like falling into a puddle, every morning. This shouldn't feel like a normal place. It's not.

The MSF clinic is near the entrance to the camp. Around it, bamboo shelters occupy every possible patch of hillside. The low-lying rice paddies of the local farmers remain carefully undisturbed. Once inside the clinic our staff welcome me with their own smiles. Shouted greetings are exchanged, and laughs, as I bungle simple Bangla.

I've been at the clinic almost every day. There is an outpost deeper

ABOVE: MSF staff meet at a healthcare facility in Cox's Bazar to discuss care for Rohingya refugees.

in the camp. There we aim to provide qualified advice and essential medicines for patients unable to traverse the tricky path to our crowded clinic. We hope it also gives us some extra eyes, as we are watchful for outbreaks. Cholera, measles and diphtheria are all possible. The walk out to the outpost meanders past shelters dense with people. I am met with intense stares and bright smiles, side by side.

Children account for more than their fair share of smiles. We are seeing more children wasted to the point of SAM. A child with SAM is 10 times more likely to die from common camp afflictions, such as diarrhoea or respiratory infections.

The incongruity of my daily pattern is disorientating. How is it possible to simultaneously delight in the encounters with patients while mourning the circumstances they endure? Where is the hope in dire,

"

My smile is reliably arrested upon seeing the camp again. Tarpaulin shelters stacked on hills where people proudly battle both the elements and poverty. Is it still right to smile? I don't know. It's reliably unsettling. Like falling into a puddle, every morning. This shouldn't feel like a normal place. It's not.

tragic circumstances? It must come from those we meet and those we work with and for on a daily basis. Writer Czesław Miłosz said human reason was a friend of hope, but I'm not sure it is enough. The irreverence in laughter, in joy and in smiles, I think, is essential.

The work itself is important for the morbidity and mortality avoided, whether that's individual or population medicine. Inherent also is the affirmation of the patient as someone deserving care. But amid the stresses of providing clinical care in a resource-constrained context, laughter can seem a guilty pleasure or even heresy. But laughter and smiles are a human trait as fundamental as hope.

Despite it all, I smile as I close my eyes on the drive out from the clinic. The long days mean I'm ready to fall asleep at a moment's notice. In this drowsy reverie I recall another patient from the afternoon, a four-year-old boy. It sounded absurd when he came back asking for the fishes, but the clinic staff knew what he meant. Two days earlier he had been transfixed by clownfish on a mobile phone, with his dad talking to him and feeding him lychee lollies while we provided wound care for a burn. He was here today to have his dressing changed. And while they won't heal the burn, I feel the smiles, the lollies and even the clownfish are essential to his care. •

Evan O'Neill

MSF staff member Tanbin Muftah observes from a high point a refugee camp in Cox's Bazar, south-east Bangladesh

A view of Melbourne's Swanston Street as life drains from the central business district during the COVID-19 pandemic.

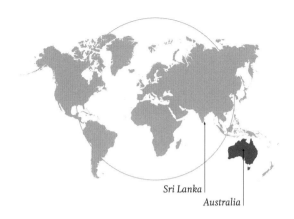

Sri Lanka

Australia

How many cases today, Dad?

AMAALI LOKUGE

Sri Lankan born Amaali Lokuge is an emergency physician at the Royal Melbourne Hospital in Victoria, Australia. She is also a freelance writer for *The New York Times*.

The colourful face-shields pinned to the wall look like abstract art. He wonders how many aerosolised COVID particles have settled on them, waiting to be inhaled. There is so much speculation and theory, and so little fact. The anxiety is palpable as everyone double and triple-checks their personal protective equipment (PPE).

The doctor 'chat' on his phone lights up with another PPE question. He observes without comment as the thread escalates towards hysteria. He writes and re-writes his message three times as the conversation veers and detours. His text, meant to be reassuring, in the end sounds like politically correct propaganda and mutes the discussion – at least for now.

A nurse leans against the counter next to him, waiting for an ECG to print. Her body sags as a sigh escapes; it's only 11:30am. He scrolls through the list of patients in the department: of the four with COVID, three are deteriorating and unlikely to survive. Through the curtain in the room opposite, he sees a nurse hold an iPad in front of a patient as their family says goodbye from the waiting room. The nurse is determinedly looking into the corner of the room, her eyes filled with tears. But she can't close her ears to the words and slowly the tears fall, drenching her mask. A passing orderly silently takes the iPad from her hands and motions for her to leave.

The next patient to be seen is an elderly woman with COVID. Her oxygen saturation is dangerously low at 70 per cent. Outside the cubicle, he puts on a new gown and gloves, watching through the window as the woman struggles to stand, spitting angry words at her daughter. The young woman keeps glancing in his direction as though willing him to rescue her from her mother's tirade. He wonders why she has been allowed in when visitors have been banned to stop the spread of the disease.

It takes an age to get through the airlock; he checks his PPE while he waits for one door to close and the other to open. His hand goes up to adjust his glasses as they slide down his nose and he panics as his fingers hit the face shield instead. He needs to be more mindful. Just like landing a Boeing 747 he had told the junior doctors yesterday; except, in the emergency department, it's like doing that in a cockpit full of noise and interruptions. He wonders how many of his colleagues will get infected, but abruptly halts this train of thought before it reaches the natural conclusion of how many will end up in ICU.

He shouts out his introduction when he enters the room and it sounds grating, but he knows people struggle to hear him through the PPE. His voice echoes in his mouth at the best of times; with the mask and face shield, it's like trying to project through triple-glazed windows. The patient's

She wants to go home – she doesn't believe she has COVID,' the young woman explains. 'She thinks it's all a conspiracy. She doesn't see that she's so unwell.

daughter gratefully interrupts her mother to translate his words.

'She wants to go home - she doesn't believe she has COVID', the young woman explains. 'She thinks it's all a conspiracy. She doesn't see that she's so unwell.' His heart sinks as he contemplates the complex discussion he will need to have with the interpreter on a conference call - a circular conversation devoid of nuance as the subtext gets lost in translation. Deferring the inevitable he initiates COVID treatments and leaves to organise the interpreter. The interaction feels empty and cold, so much

ABOVE: Emergency department nurses receive a phone call about an incoming patient.

emotion and perception destroyed by the mask and face shield, any intimacy lost by the distance enforced by the fear of infection.

The charge nurse calls to tell him of an imminent trauma: a 19-year-old, pedestrian struck by a tram, intubated at the scene, low blood pressure. The team is already assembling outside one of the trauma bays, adjusting the velcro straps of the heavy lead shields, positioning the ultrasound machine, setting out chest tubes and checking drugs.

The patient arrives before he can prepare the team. CPR is in progress. The compressions are paused while chest tubes are placed and a blood

transfusion is started. The right side of the patient's face is grossly distorted. The anaesthetist checks his pupils as a pulse returns and a weak blood pressure is recorded. The trauma consultant turns abruptly to him as the patient's matted hair is brushed away revealing broken bone and the tissue beneath. He asks the nurses for inotropic drugs to stabilise the blood pressure, and someone straps the patient's thick, tattooed arm to the board to insert an arterial line.

The charge nurse stands silently next to him as the team moves the patient to the CT scanner. 'The family is outside', she says in a sombre voice. 'There's at least 20 of them.' He nods, meeting her meaningful look, making the connection between the patient's Polynesian appearance and the mass of family gathered outside.

The mother and aunt are already crying when he arrives at the relatives' room, cheeks touching, tears mingling as they loudly voice their anguish. The patient's sister had witnessed the crash and he's relieved that the family already apprehends the worst. The trauma consultant calls to tell him of the CT result and his words, when he relays this to the family, only confirm their fears. His voice trails away and the silence is broken by a long, collective wail.

ABOVE: A tram in Melbourne's city centre.

The charge nurse comes in to reinforce the hospital policy that prevents visitors from entering the emergency department and the family relents to her authority. The defiance of the younger members dissipates as the older ones collapse with grief. He gratefully bolts out of the room as his phone rings again, leaving the nurse to deal with the logistics. He forgoes lunch to speak with the elderly COVID patient and the interpreter. In the end, he convinces the patient to stay. Her daughter beams at him as he turns to leave, oblivious to the drama playing out just a few cubicles away.

" 'I'm glad you've appointed another deputy director,' she writes. 'I was worried what we would do if you got sick.'

A whisper passes through the emergency department, stilling the usual chaos, while he writes his notes at the computer. The wailing outside gives way to a melancholy song when the young patient's ventilator is switched off. A nurse tells him that a security guard has jammed open the sliding doors to the emergency department, to let the song in. Fragile voices of children crack as they try to keep tune with their aunts and mothers. A Polynesian song resonates through the department for 20 minutes, filling the void of the silenced monitors in the patient's room.

He peels off his PPE late in the afternoon, unable to face another patient for the day. He rubs the alcohol into his hands, changes his mask, cleans the face shield and puts it back on. Before climbing the stairs to the administration area, he washes his hands again, reflecting that he has never been so clean or felt so paranoid at the same time. His email opens to more than 100 unread messages and he scrolls through them absently. He opens one from a colleague who has been particularly stressed about COVID.

'I'm glad you've appointed another deputy director', she writes. 'I was worried what we would do if you got sick …'

'Do I look fragile?' He writes back in jest without considering, then slumps in his chair wondering whether she is right to be concerned.

He completes his handover in the administration area so that he doesn't have to don the PPE again. The afternoon shift doctors are unusually subdued as they head down the stairs to the emergency department.

He wonders how such a little girl could deal with so much death. An infinite sorrow that he can't disentangle sinks a little deeper in his gut.

He leans his bike against the wall and takes off his helmet. The verandah is messy with discarded shoes and rollerblades. The bag for helmets is overflowing and his drops off and bounces along the ground, as though trying to escape the chaos. His wife has spent the day at home schooling the children and he knows the angst she would have felt each time she stepped out the front door - the untidy alcove like a visual representation of this moment in their lives.

The peace of home envelopes him as he steps in the front door. His watch pings with another message and he feels like throwing it against the wall. The cats circle his calves, mewling as their tails curl and caress. From deep inside, the rumble of children's voices and the clink of dishes draws him into their midst.

'Daddy's home!' his youngest chimes, her voice bright with anticipation.

'How many cases today, Dad?' his eldest asks, looking up from his phone. The mood changes and stiffens. His wife meets his eyes over the tops of the children's heads. He would go to her, put his arms around her and gather her warmth to him, but she glances away. He realises she doesn't have the energy to look after him today.

'Yeah Dad, how many died?' His youngest asks her eyes saucer-like with concern. 'Twenty-one in Victoria, darling', he replies, reaching out to touch her silky hair. She leans back into his palm, processing the number, her reaction unfathomable. He wonders how such a little girl could deal with so much death. An infinite sorrow that he can't disentangle sinks a little deeper in his gut.

'Fourteen hundred died in the US today,' his eldest says, scrolling through the Johns Hopkins website. The children run with the threads of the conversation while he looks on helplessly. As though sensing his distress his wife turns, leaning back against the cupboards, drying her hands with a cloth. Her tired eyes seek out his sad ones. Infinity seems to expand in the moment, and he feels the worries recede and scatter.

He collects the scene like a pebble and stores it away for later, or maybe just for tomorrow. •

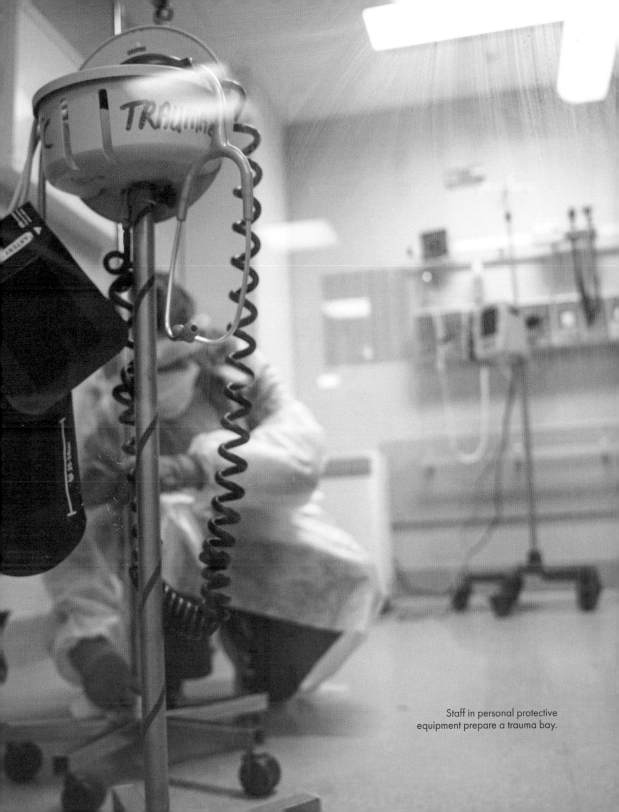

Staff in personal protective
equipment prepare a trauma bay.

A colourful sulfuric
stream flows across
the rocky surface of
Whakaari/White Island.

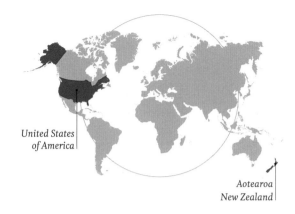

United States
of America

Aotearoa
New Zealand

The fellowship of Whakaari

KELLY PHELPS

Kelly Phelps trained in emergency medicine in the United States of America and has lived in Aotearoa New Zealand since 2009. She works as a senior emergency consultant at Whakatane Hospital.

On December 9, 2019, a small volcanic island named Whakaari/ White Island in Aotearoa New Zealand's Bay of Plenty erupted. Of the 47 people visiting the island, 22 lost their lives.

Eleven hours 22 minutes. That is the estimated time it takes to re-watch Peter Jackson's blockbuster film trilogy, *Lord of the Rings*. Tolkien's climatic drama features heroes and battles, tears and sorrow, and themes of man versus nature; yet it is still fantasy.

Twenty-one hours. That is the estimated amount of time that Whakatane Hospital, in Aotearoa New Zealand, was engaged in its own epic battle with a volcano. Whakaari is real.

Our tale begins just east of 'The Shire'. As summer holidays spring to life, one can imagine vacationing hobbits surfing on boogie boards, elves exploring the native flora and fauna along Toi's track, and dwarves quenching their thirst at the local watering hole. Old wizards might be puffing Longbottom Leaf with community elders and learning about the local legends. Legends of moving mountains in the night, jealousy and heartbreak, brave ancestral men and women, and the transfer of fire that makes up New Zealand's geothermal volcanic landscapes.

At 2:11pm, a burst of ash and steam exploded out of Whakaari. The volcano had erupted.

The Whakatane Hospital's emergency department received the phone call: White Island has erupted with tourists ashore. Expect to receive casualties; number not yet known.

The shift-duty doctor and emergency department team activated our mass casualty plan. Light the Beacons of Gondor! Just as in Peter Jackson's depiction, the call for help was swiftly heard across the hospital, across the community (and eventually across the North Island). It was answered from across the Cook Strait and over the Southern Alps to the South Island of New Zealand, then across the Tasman Sea to Australia, and even across the Pacific to North America.

Fortify the keep. Preparation of the hospital: empty the emergency department of current patients, empty the waiting room, make room in ICU, make room in surgical theatre.

Ready yourselves. Grab armour, shields, and arrows. Or rather, coloured vests, protective gear, medications, syringes, and bandages.

Prepare your legions. Triage team stationed at the front doors. Resuscitation teams formed and assigned bed spaces. Security lined the perimeter. An incident command was assembled.

> **" The Whakatane Hospital's emergency department received the phone call: White Island has erupted with tourists ashore. Expect to receive casualities; number not yet known.**

Insert director's scene in the emergency department: shoulder-to-shoulder actors and volunteered extras stood at attention, all eyes and ears were turned towards the leaders, awaiting instructions and updates. First responders prepared to meet the boat containing the casualties, just 4 kilometres away at the wharf.

Our fellowship was as varied as Frodo's. Frodo had a wizard, a dwarf, an elf, hobbit friends, and brave men. Each had unique gifts that they brought to the table; all were willing to work for the common goal.

We had emergency department doctors, junior doctors, surgeons, emergency department nurses, nurses from other wards, anaesthetists, pharmacists, the radiology department, security, orderlies, Maori health services, social workers, administrative support staff, physiotherapists, occupational therapists, local general practitioners, paediatricians,

obstetricians, internists, lab technicians, victim support, cleaners, biomedical and site engineers and so many more. It is impossible to name them all. Our St John Ambulance officers arrived like the Riders of Rohan, wearing green uniforms. Our common goal? To do the best that we possibly could.

Our first patients began to arrive. While Peter Jackson depicts chaos on the silver screen - to the actors each movement was known, practised, and organised. Although the hospital may have only prepared mass casualty events on paper and in drills, and casualties on a much smaller scale, the real-life depiction kept rolling. Everyone had a job to do. Organised chaos. Seemingly an oxymoron, but an apt description of what was happening.

Patients arrived three or four at a time, via ambulance or by helicopter. The severity and critical conditions of our patients was quickly recognised. Analgesics, airways, stabilisation and comforting words became our main priority. Every room in our emergency department transformed into a resuscitation bay.

Whereas our emergency department textbooks tell us to 'reassess airway' frequently for burns patients, our staff weren't thinking merely within the confines of a clinical instruction handbook. Instead, they adopted a 'keep-them-talking' and 'keep-them-comforted' modus operandi. Staff and patients alike swapped stories about where they were from, family and children, hobbies, and where else they had the visited in New Zealand.

Their tale continued as patients were transferred to surgical theatres or across the hall to our intensive care unit. Everyone worked together. The moment when the calvary arrived happened just like in the movies. Help from our big sister hospital Tauranga (90 kilometres away) brought more doctors, more resuscitation equipment, more controlled drugs. The Great Eagles of Middle Earth arrived in the form of medical transport aircraft and transfer teams from around the country.

The initial stabilisation was not enough, not in a small, provincial hospital. The logistics of who went where and when was what kept critically injured patients alive following the initial scene. The quick-thinking and comprehensive airlift was an amazing feat for all of New Zealand. The experts rapidly delivered patients to tertiary centres, to ensure they were in the best places to care for their conditions.

Cut to 'Behind the Scenes': often not talked about in mass casualty planning is the contribution of our non-medical personnel. Family and victim support from our social workers, cultural support, and our mental health workers was a massive undertaking, especially when most of the patients were from overseas. Their skills were truly valuable and heroic.

Now remember, I mentioned 21 hours.

Twenty-one hours was from the time the hospital was notified of the event, to when our last patient was transferred from our hospital campus. A brief stillness settled over the hospital – before the media and the politicians arrived. In that time, our team restocked supplies, and vacuumed ash from the air vents. The first support activities began. Activity continued around Whakaari, but the hospital needed to prepare for business as usual, for the next casualties of another normal day.

Epilogue

In the eleventh hour, Frodo had destroyed the ring with the help from his loyal friends. There were hugs and tears for those they lost along the way, and congratulations for a job well done. But do you remember the scene at the end when Frodo starts rubbing at the scar on his shoulder caused by the ring wraith in the first movie? Some scars take a long time to heal.

We may still have elven magic here in New Zealand, but it can take many forms. Some came in the form of our specialists in the burn centres who continued the intensive care for patients. Some magic came from dedicated and tireless mental crisis workers who worked with us to debrief. Some magic was delivered by our families and friends who recognised our needs and continued to reach out and support us.

That beacon that spread across the globe? Colleagues from around the country, Australia and Canada came to help us – to give our staff a chance to debrief and recover, and to help our tertiary colleagues continue to care for patients.

How do you recover from an event such as Whakaari? It has affected our patients, our patients' loved ones, ourselves, our loved ones, our hospital staff, our community, our nation.

I've been asked that question, and I very much wish I knew the answer. Perhaps we will bulk up our mass casualty plan under the recovery heading. What have we tried? Feeding a whole lot of hungry staff snacks and pizza during the event. Gathering on the night of the event to let staff know that this was going to be really, really hard and will affect you individually somehow or other, and that is OK. Prayer times initiated by our Maori community. Reminder emails and texts with offerings of free counselling. Bringing in kittens and puppies to cuddle. Arranging for a safe, protected place at the local watering hole for all involved: first responders, police, fire brigade, civil defence, Maori community workers, and hospital staff. Hugs and tears in the hallways. 'Are-you-OK?' check-ins via text or email. Diligence on who is safe to continue to work and who needs time off, if possible. Awareness of post-traumatic stress disorder symptoms in ourselves and our staff.

> "
> Colleagues from around the country, Australia and Canada came to help us – to give our staff a chance to debrief and recover ...

We have also planned debriefs for individual departments for the hospital as a whole and created a rippling effect through our District Health Board and Civil Defence inter-agency, and New Zealand Health, to encompass the nation.

Years later, our collective voices continue to advocate for the importance of recovery and learnings from that fateful day so that we can better serve our community. We now focus on hospital employee wellness programs, lectures at conferences, work to develop relationships with public services and emergency planning, and nurture a supportive workforce. I am so proud to be a part of Whakatane Hospital and our community. May we all continue to heal and support one another. Our hearts go out to our courageous and brave patients still fighting the good fight, as well as to those mourning those whom we have lost.

Some scars take a long time to heal. ●

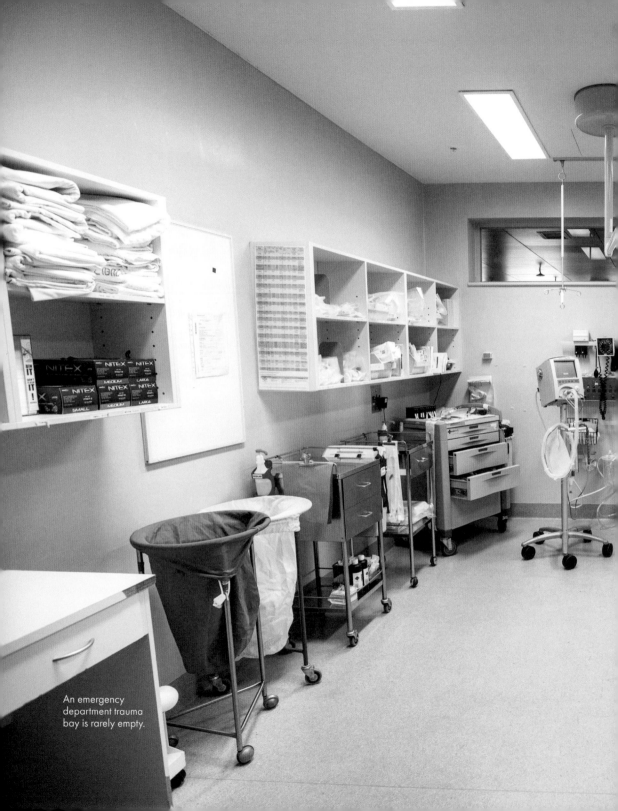

An emergency department trauma bay is rarely empty.

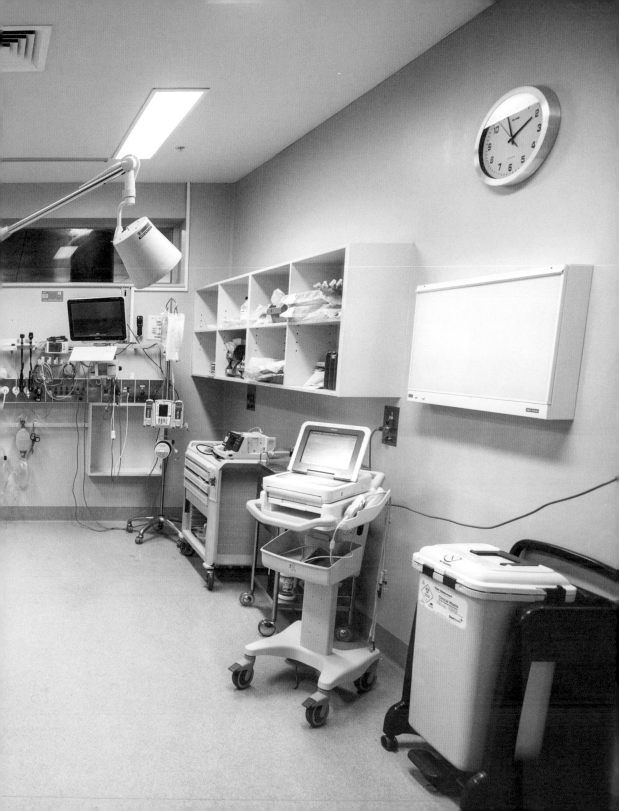

A Palestinian woman walks amidst debris in Gaza City.

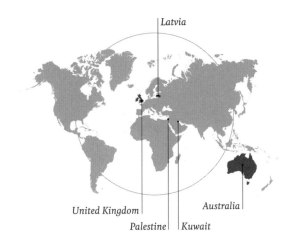

United Kingdom | Australia | Latvia | Palestine | Kuwait

Palestine, walking the line

NATALIE THURTLE AND MOHAMMED ABU MUGHIASIB

Natalie Thurtle is an emergency physician who has worked for Médecins Sans Frontières (MSF) intermittently since 2008. From January 2020 to August 2021, she was the medical coordinator in Palestine. She has since returned to clinical practice in Australia.

Mohammed Abu Mughiasib was born in Kuwait to a Palestinian family. He studied medicine in Latvia, graduating in 1998, and arrived in Palestine (Gaza) in 2000. He has worked for MSF for 20 years and was appointed deputy medical coordinator for MSF in Palestine in 2020.

10 May 2021:
NT: 'Just to update you we will be supporting clinically at a trauma stabilisation point in response to unrest in Jerusalem from now – I've got a team and some eprep stock, heading there now so I'll be a bit offline.'
MM: 'Take care and stay safe. 3 kids dead now from strike in North Gaza.'
NT: 'I saw. Sorry for that.'
MM: 'Nine dead now, some shrapnel and abdo injuries.'
NT: 'K. Let me know if you are planning to support Ministry of Health.'
MM: 'Only 2 cases referred.'
NT: 'Good. Copy.'

12 May 2021:
MM: 'Stock of blood bank will be in shortage in a few days.'
NT: 'We are sourcing blood bags.'
MM: 'Good. Blood bank in Gaza main provider is lacking funds for a while.'

13 May 2021:
MM: 'One hundred and three dead, 27 children, 580 wounded, paediatric surgeon still needed.'
NT: 'Working on it. Thanks for clarifying.'

13 May 2021 video message:
MM: 'Here's our office. Here's the balcony you know where we sit to have our coffee. Here's the place which was bombed across the street. Looks like they are trying to find people under the rubble.'

14 May 2021 voice message:
MM: 'News not confirmed. They called the tower that Ayman (MSF project coordinator) lives in to evacuate, in one hour they will bomb it. Shit.'
NT: 'Shit.'

17 May 2021:
NT: 'Morning. Hope you are OK. I'm about to do CNN interview. Any update from your side from overnight? I got that they damaged the COVID PCR testing centre.'
MM: 'Palestinian Children's Relief Fund office was destroyed during a strike, the MoH building collateral damage at the central lab, the night was heavy as yesterday, they finished the last strike at 6am.'
NT: 'Thanks that's helpful. Sorry to hear. Try to rest this morning.'

17 May 2021:
MM: 'Team saw 40 patients in clinic today'!
NT: 'Awesome! Mabruk (well done)'!

These messages are some of the thousands of communications between Médecins Sans Frontières' deputy medical coordinator Mohammed Abu (known as Abu Abed) and medical coordinator Natalie Thurtle around the conflict escalation in Palestine including the 11-day aerial bombardment of Gaza in May 2021. Abu Abed is Palestinian and has worked with MSF in Palestine for almost 20 years. Natalie is British/Australian and has worked intermittently with MSF in different countries for 13 years, the last two of which were in Palestine.

ABOVE: People clear
debris after an Israeli
airstrike destroyed the
residential tower in
Gaza City.

Gaza is a strip of land of just 365 square kilometres. During the bombardment it sustained more than 1500 airstrikes. The borders to Gaza were completely closed and allowed no movement of supplies and essential personnel. Natalie and other team members were stuck in Jerusalem, unable to enter until after the ceasefire, whilst Abu Abed and colleagues in Gaza were under immense pressure.

There were 260 deaths in Gaza during this period, of which 66 were children (UN data), and more than 2000 people were injured, one third of whom required hospital treatment. The main MSF trauma/burns outpatient clinic in Gaza city was severely damaged by a proximal aerial strike. After a structural integrity assessment, the team re-opened the damaged clinic within 48 hours, providing essential services to the existing cohort of complex patients and newly injured individuals at some personal risk. MSF also continued surgical activities in Northern Gaza.

There was no ceasefire during this time; there was no humanitarian corridor.

This may be considered emergency care at its most essential, and it's most perilous.

First do no harm - *Primum non nocere*

The concept of humanitarian aid is often rightly scrutinised. Is it corrupt? Is it overly bureaucratic? Is it colonial? Is it racist? Sometimes it is all those things. However, as the situation just describes, there remains an imperative, even in very narrow spaces such as Gaza, not to ignore oppression, not to walk past suffering, not to turn away from the injured. If we do, we somehow accept such inhumanity, validate it, 'other' it.

Whether or not aid delivery is problematic at a given point in time, or in a given location, is both structural and, at present, at least partially person(s)-dependent. MSF has a model whereby short-term international staff work with longer-term local staff, though the organisation has a tendency to place international staff in a position of power, which may or may not be appropriate to their skill level. International staff are meant to add capacity, to provide technical knowledge and upskilling where it is lacking and mental energy where local staff are exhausted by living through the same experiences as the patients they are working with. This can work well, or not, depending on those involved.

Abu Abed has worked with a multitude of international colleagues in Palestine over the last two decades. They have had different approaches

ABOVE: In May 2021, MSF started supporting the Palestinian Red Crescent Society in Jerusalem to assess and stabilise hundreds of injured Palestinians.

and communication styles that local staff are often expected to understand and adapt to. Their contract is often not long enough for them to grasp the cultural and political context. They rely on local staff to brief and re-brief them, steer them, re-orient them, including during times of acute emergency. Context-naive international staff in positions of power may easily bypass or invalidate recommendations from senior national staff, even straying into abuse such as activation of vexatious disciplinary proceedings.

Shifting to the broader context, Gaza is one of the most restricted places on the planet. The well-documented detrimental health impacts of the Israeli blockade, combined with the socioeconomic conditions driven by it are immense, even before a large escalation in violence. The health infrastructure is very fragile – a paper house. A gust of wind from a COVID wave, or a hurricane of intense aerial bombardment and it can wobble and fall. There are also many humanitarian actors jostling for space and the authorities have a lot of competing priorities, especially during a war. Two million people are trapped in 'the world's largest jail'. It is dense in every sense of the word.

> " The concept of humanitarian aid is often rightly scrutinised. Is it corrupt? Is it overly bureaucratic? Is it colonial? Is it racist? Sometimes it is all those things.

So, how does MSF add value to emergency care during an evolving acute-on-chronic emergency in a notoriously complex context with high security risk, in a way that tries to avoid perpetuating the colonial threads of humanitarian aid?

It wasn't perfect, but perfect may be considered the enemy of good in emergency care. We landed on a few key points:

1. Protect our regular activities
Had the aerial bombardment continued longer term, it may have totally overwhelmed Gaza's healthcare infrastructure. We prepared to support should that occur, lining up/repurposing additional clinical trauma human resources in discussion with the Ministry of Health, and focused on getting our regular trauma/burns clinic and surgical activities up and running during the bombardment. Thankfully the ceasefire held, and we moved into the fall-out phase.

Palestine is a chronic emergency. This flare in conflict was thankfully short. One focus was to steer our organisation away from being too reactive and starting new activities in response to the escalation. MSF ordinarily sees 5000 burns cases a year in Gaza that no-one else has the

A Palestinian man stands inside a destroyed apartment in Gaza City.

"Over time, and having experienced four wars since 2008, their bodies and minds are degraded, and some staff prefer to stay at home rather than socialise.

capacity to follow up. We run a complex multidisciplinary trauma and osteomyelitis program that the Ministry of Health does not have the resources to manage. We support with COVID case management. We are in the process of consolidating and expanding our mental health activities. Horrific flares in violence like this feed patients into all these programs, and our post-ceasefire assessment highlighted particularly big gaps in mental health provision. We aimed to maintain and reinforce our existing programs rather than start new emergency interventions with limited capacity.

Where we landed, overall, was to take a breath and hold the line. To come back to our regular activities and to reinforce them, to reinvest in them.

2. Protect and invest in our staff
A strategy of protecting regular activities meant protecting and investing in our staff, including guarding against an influx of extra managerial international staff during the acute emergency as they may be more likely to start an activity or cause disruption. Rather, existing international staff and, more importantly, senior local staff were elevated and supported.

MSF has more than 200 staff in Gaza. They all went through 11 days of hell being bombed. For most it was not the first time. People were devastated and damaged. It is said by some that they cannot call it recovery, that, post-ceasefire, they are merely in a paused situation, preparing for the next wave of violence. Mind and body are taking a rest and regrouping for next time. Over time, and having experienced four wars since 2008, their bodies and minds are degraded, and some staff prefer to stay at home rather than socialise. Some trauma manifests as back pain, neck pain and either loss of productivity, or overworking to forget.

Gaza is not an isolated event and to offer support on that basis would have been reductionist. In practice this meant giving space for psychological diffusion, providing high-quality psychologists and therapy for those who wished to engage, long breaks for those who desired them, support, comfort and recognition, both for the debilitating condition of living in Gaza, and for the work done day in, day out, including slowing the pace of that work. Over time, structural improvements to working conditions are also key.

3. Change the narrative
Working on the frontline during this escalation gave MSF, and us as individuals in medical coordination, the credibility to speak out about what we witnessed. The mainstream narrative is often pro-Israeli or,

'It's complicated', when in reality it's not that complicated. The solution may not be easily apparent, but the pathway that led to this point, and the real situation on the ground in May was frequently obscured by manipulation and politicisation of information, meaning that external observers consider the situation more complex than it actually is.

Palestine is occupied. Palestinians are treated at best like second-class citizens, repeatedly bombed and caged and traumatised and restricted from growth. Some are unsurprisingly radicalised as a result of deep disenfranchisement; however the vast majority are not, and continue to live calmly under oppression, resisting peacefully and hoping for the world to see what is happening in Palestine. Part of our responsibility in Gaza was to witness, and to use the platforms that we are privileged to have to share information and counter the narrative of complexity. To attempt to meet this aim, the team did more than 200 interviews in nine languages in May and June 2021.

4. Work with the Ministry of Health
Working alongside the Palestinian Ministry of Health in a diplomatic and transparent way is key to limiting the colonial shadows from humanitarian agencies. Whilst the ministry's capacity has been severely curtailed by the blockade and surrounding factors, they remain the main healthcare provider in Gaza and are used to and effective at leading during conflict emergencies. Relationships during this chaotic period were more important than ever and were expertly held together by long-serving local staff who managed complex negotiations.

Going forward
The historical infrastructure of humanitarian aid organisations in emergency care may be considered, unfortunately, a microcosm of the same structures that created the need for humanitarian aid in emergency care. Gross inequity runs across lines of race and ethnicity, structural violence and colonial attitudes.

However, as individuals we have some power, and some responsibility, to try to move in ways that do not perpetuate that, to not harm whilst we 'help'. The humanitarian sector may be structured inequitably, but as staff within that structure we can change some aspects of that at the micro level. Investing in, supporting and recognising the capacity, institutional memory and leadership of our local staff, as well as, in Gaza, acknowledging their deep and ongoing trauma, is a fundamental path to providing effective care for our patients. •

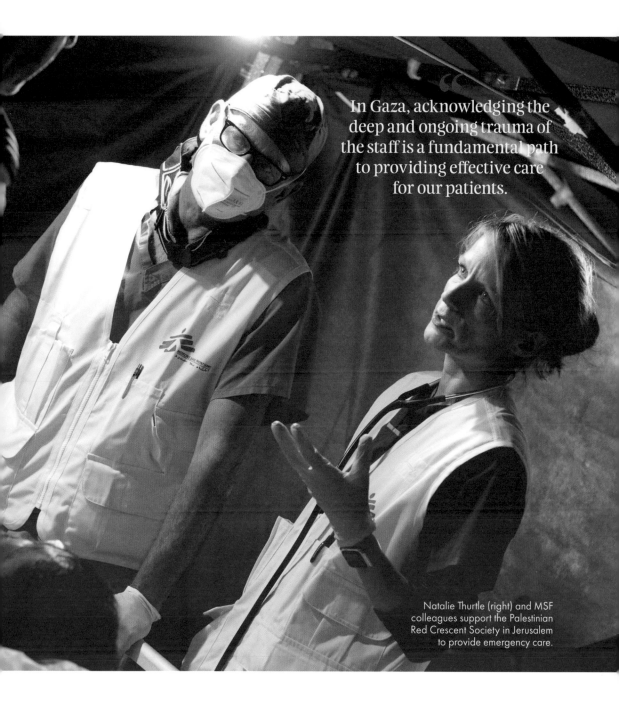

> In Gaza, acknowledging the deep and ongoing trauma of the staff is a fundamental path to providing effective care for our patients.

Natalie Thurtle (right) and MSF colleagues support the Palestinian Red Crescent Society in Jerusalem to provide emergency care.

Sister Edith Namba and visiting emergency nurse JP Miller update the staffing allocations board at Mount Hagen Provincial Hospital Emergency Department in Papua New Guinea.

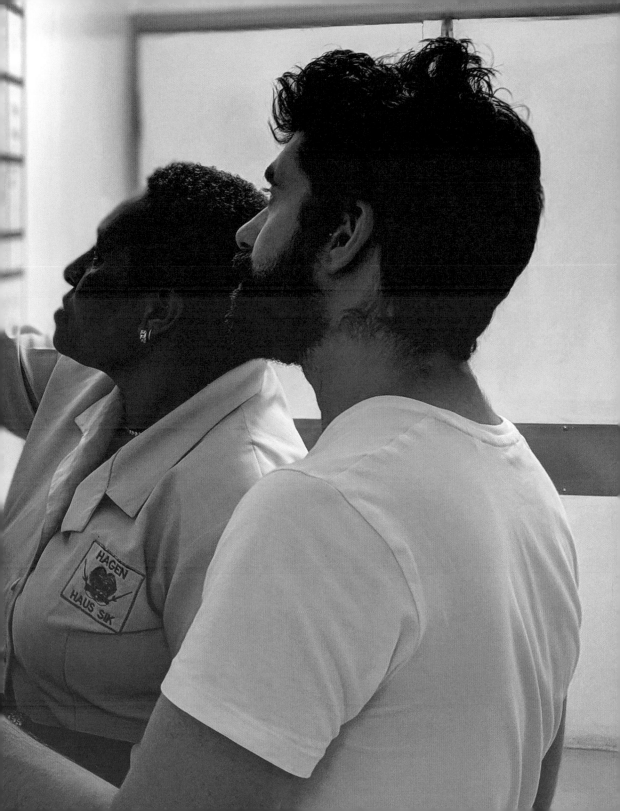

Stalls along the street in downtown Yangon, Myanmar.

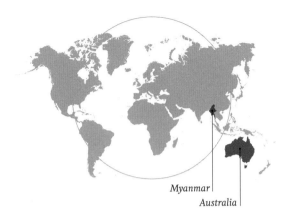

Myanmar
Australia

The pulse has gone

ROSANNE SKALICKY

Rosanne (Rose) Skalicky is a senior emergency medicine specialist based in in South Australia, and an honorary professor at the University of Medicine 1 in Yangon, Myanmar. She worked alongside local colleagues to develop emergency medicine in Myanmar from 2013 to 2021.

'The pulse has gone! Start CPR and mouth to mouth!'
Only minutes before, the professor of radiology had been speaking passionately, sharing his views with the assembled crowd. The other professors and medical administrators listened attentively, awaiting their turn to respond.

The meeting had been scheduled to discuss the emerging role of emergency medicine at the Yangon General Hospital. The four newly appointed emergency medicine consultants had been allowed to attend, but not speak. After all, this new discipline was still too young to know its place alongside the more mature specialties.

The discussion so far had oscillated from scepticism to encouragement, and the room was abuzz with opinions and perspectives. Having concluded his speech, the radiology professor sat down. All of a sudden, he was silent. Too silent. A pale hue washed over him, and then his complexion rapidly turned to white.

In that moment, the four emergency consultants sprang into action. The hospital boardroom was not the well-resourced resuscitation cubicle they were used to, but as they took control of the desperate situation it was clear they were in their element. A defibrillator was summoned and rapidly conveyed from the administration area downstairs. On this occasion, process delays worked in the favour of the emergency medicine consultants and the radiology professor. The machine had been sitting idle in the medical superintendent's office, waiting to be commissioned and deployed to the emergency department.

'Stand clear, shock given', the machine intoned. 'Start CPR.'

Minutes later, a pulse was felt and the groans that emerged from the collapsed professor were met with cheers and praise. With the role of emergency care so powerfully demonstrated, the meeting was suspended. Emergency medicine was here!

> While a moment like this could not be choreographed, it was one of many that highlighted the potential value of emergency medicine in Myanmar.

While a moment like this could not be choreographed, it was one of many that highlighted the potential value of emergency medicine in Myanmar. The outcomes, however, were not always so positive. Some of the pioneering emergency medicine doctors shared their stories with me.

One trainee, during her junior doctor years in a township hospital, was expected to receive and admit all patients, regardless of severity, to their respective wards. Triage – the sorting of patients – was not practised; it was first in, first seen. One day during her shift, she encountered five patients, all family, from the same roll-over car accident. She and her colleague saw the patients; the one with the abdominal injury went to the surgical ward, the one with the head injury to the neurosurgical ward and the ones with broken bones to the orthopaedic ward.

The following day she heard that the patient in the neurosurgical ward had died. Why? The head injury was only mild; that wasn't supposed to happen. Sadly, the patient's other injuries were not so minor. With guilt and regret, and self-recrimination mounting, she concluded that patients like these should be seen by experts. Hearing that emergency medicine had commenced at Yangon General Hospital, she flew from her town to Yangon to talk to the professor of emergency medicine. 'He inspired me. The passion in his eyes, and the type of care they were doing, made me decide that emergency care is what we need for our country, and I should be doing this.'

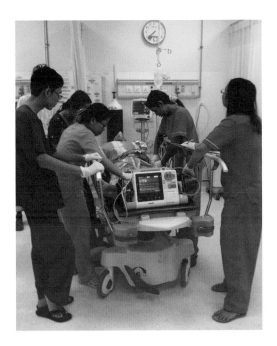

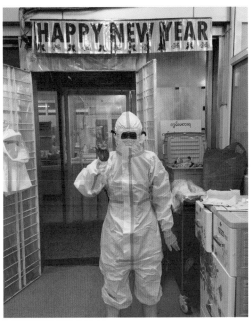

ABOVE LEFT: Emergency department staff at Yangon General Hospital.

ABOVE RIGHT: An emergency clinician welcomes the new year in personal protective equipment.

Another consultant described how, during his junior doctor years, prior to the establishment of emergency medicine, he treated many emergency patients, not really understanding what to do when they first arrived. Some lived, some died. That's just what happened. Resources were variable and, generally, he worked in isolation.

There was one particular case that stood out for him: a woman bitten by a cobra snake who went into cardiac arrest. A senior doctor, not emergency medicine trained, happened to be working with him that day, and together they intubated the patient and commenced CPR. Seeing this woman survive led him to wonder who else could be resuscitated? With a growing thirst to read and learn more about emergency care, he met with the new emergency medicine consultants in Yangon who were leading the health response for the 2013 South East Asian games. 'After that, there was nothing else I wanted to do.'

The newness of emergency medicine as a specialty, a baby among the senior disciplines of surgery and medicine, often meant that the trainees were seen as outliers and pioneers – both with good and bad connotations. However, to the emergency consultants and trainees, it was this sense of youth that banded them together, not just as a specialty but as a family.

Challenges and obstacles were something to surmount and grow from.

ABOVE: A crowd of people at a street market in Yangon, Myanmar.

I remember, as a newly arrived foreigner, being given a tour of Yangon General Hospital, viewing the space that would become the emergency department. As I entered the foyer from the roadside, I was bombarded by the smell and sounds of the chaotic receiving area. People pushing to gain a position at the front; dogs, cats and rats all mingling together with the crowds.

My brain was having difficulty envisaging the 'modern emergency department'. Yet my Myanmar colleagues were busily explaining their vision, asking questions, and articulating solutions to the challenges before them. There was no doubt that if passion alone could move things forward, then emergency medicine would soon be running and not walking.

Even as the emergency departments grew and expanded, some things were slower to catch up - like 24/7 electricity. There was a lag between developing the resuscitation area and connecting it to the back-up generator line. In the early days whenever the power went off, the room would be plunged into relative darkness. Suddenly, a multitude of phone torches would emerge so the doctors could continue intubating, and the nurses could disconnect patients from the ventilators to use manual bag valve mask systems instead. With the air conditioning off, the temperature would quickly rise to meet the hot and humid ambient conditions. Yet, my colleagues, sweat pouring down their faces, would continue managing the patients and their families, usually without missing a beat.

To my colleagues, emergency medicine was not just about providing acute care, it was about changing attitudes to care. One day, a 16-year-old girl arrived at the emergency department with a three-day history of progressive arm and leg weakness. Although she was still breathing, she couldn't speak. Shortly after arriving, her oxygen level dropped and secretions began to pool in her mouth, making her breathe noisily. Guillain-Barré, a rare and rapidly progressive neurological condition, was suspected, and the decision was made to intubate and ventilate her.

It was normal to have many family members by the bedside, even in the resuscitation room. Given the staff shortages, family members were active caregivers. In this case, this patient's family had no access to education and limited health literacy and, sensing the worse, wanted to take her home. In a low-middle income country such as Myanmar, where admission to the intensive care unit was expensive and most families had personal experience of poor outcomes, this response was common.

> " The temperature would quickly rise to meet the hot and humid ambient conditions. Yet, my colleagues, sweat pouring down their faces, would continue managing the patients.

The emergency medicine doctor noted that the patient seemed to be listening and blinking. This 16-year-old girl understood what was happening and was communicating with her eyes. She wanted treatment! The emergency medicine doctor explained the situation to the patient and mediated the consent issues with the assembled relatives. Weeks later, the girl was successfully discharged from the intensive care unit and reunited with her family.

Reflectively, the emergency medicine doctor managing this care observed that, 'In Myanmar, in most cases, management plans are made by the family and often considerations can be more about money and the burden on the family rather than patient wishes, particularly in the unconscious and those with mental and physical disabilities. I have learned that as an emergency doctor we need to talk with the patient. I consider this an important part of what we do and how we can improve care.' In the eyes of the community, this sentiment quickly became equated with emergency medicine.

The community's growing respect and appreciation for the emergency doctors and nurses was enhanced by stories of survival in situations where death was the norm. An emergency medicine consultant recounted one such story at the first Myanmar emergency medicine conference.
A 54-year-old man had been working at a construction site in Nay Pyi Taw and a large, wooden stick had struck his chest. His friends brought him to the hospital by car. Sweating profusely, complaining of chest pain and palpitations, he was quickly taken into the resuscitation area, with the eyes of those in the waiting room boring into him. With triage now an accepted practice, this man must either be a VIP or very sick to go straight in. He didn't look like a VIP, so he must be sick.

In the resuscitation room, he initially appeared to improve with treatment. His chest was tender but there was no real sign of bruising or injury. His chest x-ray showed a large heart, not uncommon in Myanmar where heart disease is widespread. The emergency medicine doctor, not convinced that it was normal, performed an ultrasound. It revealed blood in the sac around the heart, causing the right side to collapse.

As the patient's blood pressure dropped, and he once again became sweaty and pale, the emergency medicine doctor drained some of this blood from around the heart using a long needle. It was a procedure not previously performed outside the operating theatre. As the blood was extracted, the heart could fill once again. Colour and life were instantly restored.

As COVID-19 and then a military take-over became part of the history of 2020 and 2021, so did the continuing passion and dedication of the emergency doctors and nurses.

While management of thousands of COVID-19 cases demonstrated the huge clinical capacity of the emergency medicine staff; it was the care of each other as family that had the deepest impact. As numbers of cases grew and staff felt fearful of living at home and passing on the virus to family members, alternative living arrangements were made, washing machines and drying lines were set up, clothing donated, and food provided daily. When someone became ill and went into isolation, it was the emergency medicine family that provided care.

In 2021 this demonstration of compassion and great commitment was seen in all the emergency doctors: those who remained in the government hospitals to treat the public, and those who left to care for the public in regional centres, health clinics and through teleconsultations. As the Delta strain of COVID-19 hit Myanmar like a tsunami, the limited resources in many of the government hospitals, a shortage of intensive care beds as

"

While the journey of emergency care in Myanmar is still being written, the steps and stories so far reflect a cohort of dedicated doctors and nurses with great capacity and resilience.

well as a mistrust of the system, meant that many patients with COVID-19 had to be treated at home.

One Myanmar colleague reflected on this experience. 'Treating a category one, severe patient at home via telephone, without hospital facilities, is not something I thought I would ever have to do, but thankfully this patient survived.' The 60-year-old man with a history of stroke, diabetes, and atrial fibrillation, had been progressively getting sicker over four days, with fever, cough, and diarrhoea. A low blood pressure and oxygen level, fast pulse and high temperature indicated to the emergency medicine doctor, on the other end of the telephone line, that he should really be in the resuscitation room. He needed intensive care, but it was not available.

After ordering drugs, oxygen and intravenous fluids, it became apparent that a powerful medication – noradrenaline – was required to raise and maintain the patient's blood pressure. This was a drug normally used in the resuscitation room or the intensive care unit. The patient's daughter was a doctor, who was prepared to facilitate her father's care and follow the emergency medicine consultant's directions. In these circumstances, the emergency medicine doctor was willing to continue the treatment.

Anxiety was a daily companion, but by day seven the emergency medicine doctor was overjoyed that her friend's father appeared to be recovering. Short-lived, this feeling turned to angst when on day eight the patient's shock recurred. Treatment, improvement and deterioration occurred on two further occasions before he finally recovered, for good, on day 19. A happy ending.

While the journey of emergency care in Myanmar is still being written, the steps and stories so far reflect a cohort of dedicated doctors and nurses with great capacity and resilience, united in their desire and commitment to provide good care for their people. Recent events might have weakened emergency medicine's pulse, but it is far from gone. •

A view of the skyline over Delhi, India.

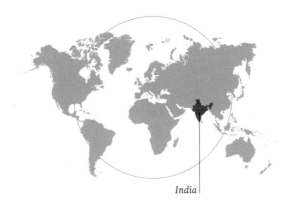

India

Mrs Indira

ANKUR VERMA

Ankur Verma has been working in emergency medicine for the last 15 years. He is currently a senior consultant in the Department of Emergency Medicine at Max Super Specialty Hospital in Patparganj, New Delhi, India.

As the world now knows, India grappled with a second wave of the COVID pandemic in early 2021. Our emergency departments, intensive care units and wards were overflowing with patients. It was a disaster at unprecedented levels.

The available resources were quickly depleted. We ran out of space, out of oxygen, out of ventilators. Wherever we turned, patients and their family members came running towards us, bursting with questions, seeking treatment for COVID and access to a hospital bed. For many, the situation was desperate.

An elderly man approached me one day as I was preparing to go home at the end of a shift. 'Does my wife have COVID? Will she die? We brought her here after all the other hospitals refused to take her in. Please save her.' He started crying, and I immediately felt guilty about something that I had absolutely no control over.

Patients were often forced to wait in ambulances for extended periods of time because the emergency department was full. We felt powerless to improve the situation. Family members would approach us and plead, 'Please just take them on chairs. We do not want them to die in an ambulance.' We took them on chairs but then were unable to provide them with oxygen. We started using portable cylinders, but we ran out of them as well. We watched these patients die, feeling utterly helpless and heartbroken. 'Thank you. You doctors are doing an incredible job', the family would say. But we felt very differently.

The elderly man waited calmly for his turn and asked me the same questions again. I took him into the counselling room, and explained the severity of his wife's condition, the unpredictable nature of COVID, and the need for hope in such times. He broke down while I was talking to him, but he understood what was happening and left. Sometimes we would counsel family members of five or six patients together because we didn't have time to update them individually.

'Your wife, your son and your husband are very, very sick. We are doing everything possible for them. Let's hope they get better', we would tell them. But we knew that many of them would not.

Every day was like this. It became routine to work overtime for the sake of our patients. Our families saw less and less of us, but they were always there to provide emotional and moral support.

> " 'Your wife, your son and your husband are very, very sick. We are doing everything possible for them. Let's hope they get better.' ... But we knew that many of them would not.

As each day passed, it seemed as though the situation only worsened, the light at the end of the tunnel fading with each fleeting moment. The cases surged to such an extent that there was no place to cremate the deceased. The city became an active funeral ground.

Early one morning, when our night team was finishing a gruelling shift, Mrs Indira was brought to our emergency department with breathlessness. Her symptoms had started an hour earlier. While she was being wheeled in, she started to gasp and soon collapsed.

The doctors who were going off duty witnessed the event. They scooped her out of the chair and ran to the resuscitation bay. CPR commenced.

After 30 minutes, her heart started beating again, but she was still not breathing on her own and hadn't regained her consciousness. We connected a ventilator and began to look for a cause. An ECG was performed, which showed that her heart was not beating as fast as it should be, a condition known as heart block. Mrs Indira needed immediate care, or

she might suffer another cardiac arrest. The staff understood the need for a temporary external pacemaker, and someone ran to get the equipment.

I felt proud of my team. They hadn't shut their eyes for a second while on duty, and they decided to stay back to help me care for this patient. COVID had made our team even closer. In some respects, we had become more like a tight-knit family than work colleagues.

The staff member soon arrived with the equipment, and we placed the external pacemaker over Mrs Indira's chest. Her heart rate improved, but only temporarily. She really needed an internal pacemaker to stabilise the situation.

After discussions with the cardiology team, the patient was prepped for the procedure, and we arranged to transfer her to the cardiac catheterisation lab - the unit that performs these types of interventions. Just before she was shifted out, the nurse stopped us.

'Doctor, Mrs Indira has tested positive for COVID.'

At that point, the cardiac catheterisation lab was unable to care for

COVID-positive patients. So Mrs Indira remained in our department, where our team inserted an internal pacemaker wire through one of the veins in her neck. It was a delicate but necessary procedure.

Mrs Indira gradually stabilised over the next couple of days. The critical shortage of inpatient beds meant that she remained with us in the emergency department; there was no capacity in the intensive care unit. She was started on COVID treatment, and her vital signs were monitored by our emergency consultants and senior nurses 24/7. Slowly, Mrs Indira's normal heart rhythm returned, and the temporary pacemaker wire was removed. Her breathing efforts improved over time, and she was taken off the ventilator.

After four days, things started to go downhill. COVID, and the medicines used to treat it, can increase blood sugar levels in certain patients. Mrs Indira was diabetic and hypertensive, and unsurprisingly her glucose readings skyrocketed. Critical electrolytes, like sodium, also started going off track. These issues soon escalated, and we had to resort to dialysis to stabilise the situation – all while she remained in the emergency department.

Just when we thought things were starting to get better, Mrs Indira surprised us. During one dialysis session she became breathless again and her oxygen levels plummeted. An x-ray showed that her left lung had collapsed due to mucous plugs in her lungs. A bronchoscope – a device that can look inside a patient's airway – was inserted, and the mucous plugs removed. Her oxygen saturation levels and x-ray subsequently improved.

We wondered whether a lack of engagement with her family was contributing.

Once we felt that she was out of the woods, we could have shifted her to a ward bed. But by this time, she had become 'our' patient, and her care trajectory was positive. We wanted to witness the 'fruits of our labor'. Her family, especially her son, was very satisfied with our team's care, and requested that she be discharged directly from the emergency department when ready.

Over time, we realised that Mrs Indira was no longer projecting a willingness to get better and might be depressed. Engaging with her became more and more difficult. She wouldn't follow commands or move her limbs when we tried to examine her. This worried our team, as everyone had invested a lot in her care.

We wondered whether a lack of engagement with her family was contributing. They had not been allowed to enter the hospital because

'Will you invite us to the wedding?' our team members asked her. 'Yes of course, you saved my life!'

of COVID restrictions, so we had been communicating primarily through video calls. We discussed the scenario and decided to allow her son, in full personal protective equipment, to visit his mother three times a day and feed her meals. We witnessed several of their conversations during these meetings.

'We love you a lot and we need you to prepare for my sister's wedding', Mrs Indira's son would say as he fed her. At first, she barely smiled, but over time she engaged more positively. We witnessed a stark change in her persona, and she finally started to interact with us. Eventually, Mrs Indira exclaimed how much she wanted to see her daughter get married once she was out of the hospital.

'Will you invite us to the wedding?' our team members asked her.

'Yes of course, you saved my life!' Mrs Indira quipped back, with a bright smile on her face. She was regaining her old self, both physically and mentally.

This progress uplifted us too, and we began extensive chest and limb physiotherapy. Her pace of recovery quickened, and she was finally discharged after a 14-day stay in our department. As expected, her family was ecstatic that she survived the ordeal. So were we.

At a time of great distress, Mrs Indira reminded us of the power of determination. Her situation initially seemed impossible. But the combination of personal willpower, family support and deep commitment of staff ensured recovery in the most challenging of circumstances.

Emergency departments were never designed to care for patients for extended periods of time. Sometimes, however, exceptional situations call for exceptional responses. This was one of those occasions.

The second COVID wave in India took a lot from us, but Mrs Indira gave us hope. Among all the death and despair of that torrid period, we found a reason to keep going. We owe her much more than she owes us. •

ACKNOWLEDGEMENTS
I would like to acknowledge Sanjay Jaiswal, Meghna Haldar, Wasil Rasool Sheikh, Amit Vishen, Rinkey Ahuja, Abbas Ali Khatai and Nilesh Prasad for contributing to this story.

Patients await care for suspected COVID-19 outside a hospital in Karnataka, India.

Homes in the suburbs
of Tegucigalpa,
the capital city of
Honduras.

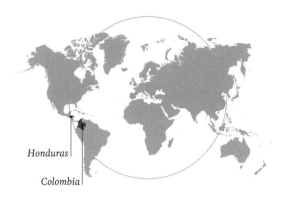

Honduras

Colombia

A unique cup of coffee

KILLIAM ARGOTE-ARAMÉNDIZ

Killiam Argote-Araméndiz is an emergency medicine specialist from the University of Antioquia in Colombia and a Beth Israel Deaconess Medical Center/Harvard Medical School disaster medicine fellow. He works as an emergency department specialist for the International Committee of the Red Cross and has been assigned to Honduras, El Salvador, Mexico, Venezuela and Ukraine.

I no longer require an alarm clock. There is another incentive. The smell, bitterness and sweetness of a dark, hot, freshly brewed cup of coffee is enough to wake me. As a Colombian, I have been drinking coffee in different presentations for as long as I can remember. This habit has become even more meaningful since I departed home, seeking a more valuable purpose in life.

It is well-known that Colombian coffee is among the best in the world. Before living in Honduras, I did not drink coffee from anywhere other than my homeland. This inflexibility left me with limited options when I was in other countries, and forced me to travel with bags of beans in my suitcase. My stay in Honduras was planned for six months and I wondered how I would replicate that moment I enjoyed each morning.

So I loaded my luggage with 3 kilograms of my favourite coffee.

My posting in Honduras was an opportunity to work with the International Committee of the Red Cross (ICRC), caring for the acutely

135

ill and injured in a low-resource setting, and had long been a career goal. During my undergraduate studies in medicine, I found myself attracted to the emergency department. The experiences of a health worker and a patient in the emergency department are incomparable to any other environment; they involve life and death, pain and relief, loneliness, companionship, and humanity.

The ultimate goal of the health worker is to restore the physical, mental, and moral integrity of those in dire need and there is no place where this is achieved in greater degree than in the emergency department. I have found a great sense of vocation and selflessness in this specialty. Working in disaster medicine has taught me how to care for hundreds of people at a time, through targeted actions that impact the present and future of the affected population.

During the first weeks in Tegucigalpa, as I was beginning to get to know the people working with the ICRC and the interlocutors from the hospital, I quickly realised that six months would not be long enough to achieve the proposed outcomes of my assignment. I also realised that the amount of coffee I brought was insufficient! Emergency medicine is not a speciality in Honduras. Reconciling the everlasting disagreement of a department divided by surgical and medical specialties into a unified, patient-centred emergency department was going to take mountains of caffeine.

> **"**
> **Working in disaster medicine has taught me how to care for hundreds of people at a time, through targeted actions that impact the present and future of the affected population.**

In 2018, the ICRC established a team to support the emergency department at Hospital Escuela, the largest referral hospital in the country. The team included a specialist nurse and doctor, a project manager and a field officer. The team changed over time, but its most significant achievements were construction of a triage and treatment building and the development of a four-colour, nurse-based routine triage system.

Just six weeks after I arrived, the COVID-19 pandemic threatened all that had been achieved. Changes were needed to respond to the rapidly evolving and growing needs. We collaborated to create a patient flow pathway for patients with suspected COVID through the emergency department, with triage and pre-triage tools. We led 30 webinars involving nursing and medical staff from the hospital and other healthcare institutions from Tegucigalpa to train them in patient care, biosafety and self-care. We also made personal protective equipment donations.

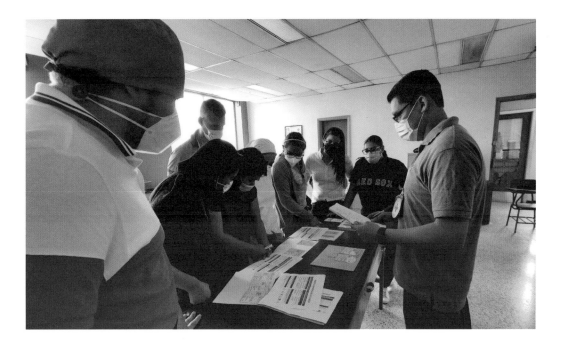

ABOVE: ICRC staff delivering mass casualty triage training.

It was a frantic six months and I soon realised that the Honduran coffee I was now drinking could also provide me the sweet, sour and bitter flavours that I thought I could only get from my Colombian brews. So, I extended my work in Honduras for a further 12 months.

We started having monthly meetings to enhance communication and further unify the emergency department leadership team. The idea of having a standardised resuscitation room had taken hold and we set up a project to equip and modify an area that could provide CPR, airway management and multi-trauma simulations to trainee doctors and general practitioners to enhance their skills. Nurses were also regularly trained and re-trained in routine triage and other essential emergency room skills as the situation changed.

Honduras is the second-largest country in Central America. It has almost 10 million inhabitants and a painful history of violence and corruption. The international publication *InSight Crime* classifies Honduras at number 41 among the most dangerous countries on the globe and reports that its homicide rate in 2019 was 41.2 per 100,000 inhabitants. Transparency International ranked the country at number 125 on its

Emergency clinicians undertake training in the Interagency Integrated Triage Tool.

corruption perception index in 2020. This scourge significantly impacts access to health services and the availability of healthcare. Against this backdrop, the nation is the fifth-largest coffee producer in the world, has a diversity of microclimates and altitudes, and its artisanal processes and preservation of coffee beans make Honduran coffee unique.

Such a history of corruption and violence has had an enormous impact on access to healthcare. Under routine conditions, hospital emergency departments are overcrowded. In recent years there have been several mass casualty incidents. In 2012 almost 400 people lost their lives in a prison fire. Other incidents include a gas explosion in the local market in Tegucigalpa, frequent protests and riots in the streets, and even street battles involving sports fans. The political situation in the country has exacerbated the unrest, resulting in a steady flow of patients with significant injuries. One of the project's main objectives was to create a mass casualty plan to improve emergency responses in this volatile setting.

"

Such a history of corruption and violence has had an enormous impact on access to healthcare. Under routine conditions, hospital emergency departments are overcrowded.

In January 2021, I put a proposition to the hospital leadership to show them the value of developing a mass casualty plan. They approved and a multidisciplinary team was formed, including clinicians and non-clinicians from different hospital departments. We addressed hospital incident command systems, conducted a hazard vulnerability analysis and assessed emergency department capacity and expansion possibilities for space, staff, and equipment. We also considered triage systems, staff safety, and the standardised response to achieve security, crowd control and the flow of patients and vehicles. The process of managing family members, unaccompanied minors, vulnerable populations, and volunteers was also discussed.

At the same time, we began training emergency department staff in mass casualty triage. The selected tool was the Integrated Interagency Triage Tool (IITT) developed by Médecins Sans Frontières, the ICRC and the World Health Organization. To date, almost 100 nurses and doctors have been trained in the system. We provided hospital incident command system training for the hospital's leadership and management. Security enforcement, emergency department crowd control and patient flow were also addressed with security staff.

An opportunity to practise the plan came to us when the Toncontín International Airport at Tegucigalpa developed a flight emergency drill and announced its selected patient referral hospital would be Hospital Escuela. With our hands full and with one week's notice, I took on the challenge of preparing the emergency department for this drill, reinforcing our mass casualty triage, our hospital incident command system and security and safety measures for staff and management.

We prepared designated areas, developed mass casualty plan triage stations and held meetings with the city's emergency response stakeholders, including the 911 coordination, police, fire brigade, the Honduran Red Cross, the airport leadership and the Permanent Emergency Commission of Contingencies.

> In true pandemic style, we were able to pivot, and the emergency department chief nurse took charge. In less than an hour, the mass casualty plan was triggered, leadership positions were activated.

A mentor once taught me that the worst thing that can happen is for a drill to be perfect, and this was no exception. We had planned to have the emergency department's chief doctor as the incident commander, but the reality of the pandemic had other plans. Six hours before the drill commenced, one of his closest family members had to be hospitalised in the ICU due to COVID-19 and he couldn't participate. In true pandemic style, we were able to pivot, and the emergency department chief nurse took charge. In less than an hour, the mass casualty plan was triggered, leadership positions were activated, designated areas were established, and 20 simulated patients were triaged and directed to treatment areas. We learned a lot from the things we did right, and even more from the ones we could improve.

After the drill, I took a couple of days off in the Honduras mountains. But, once again, reality struck. On June 17 around 8am, while I was enjoying the tartaric bitterness and nutty taste of freshly brewed Honduran coffee, a tussle between two of the most dangerous gangs in the world busted out in the maximum-security prison, located in Morocelí, El Paraíso, known as 'La Tolva'. Members of the Mara Barrio 18 (known as La 18) broke into one of the sections of the prison holding

"

It was a unique cup of Honduran coffee symbolising all the bitterness of being away from home, the sours of the long working hours, and the sweetness of having improved the emergency response.

members of the Mara Salvatrucha (known as MS-13) with a hand grenade and started shooting. As a result of this incursion, 31 patients were sent to the emergency department with gunshot and stab wounds, alongside numerous other injuries.

I received a text from my teammates saying they were on their way to the emergency department. The next text, which reached me on the mountain at 11:30am contained the most exciting news I had received so far in Honduras. My teammates informed me that everyone in the department, from porters to senior doctors, was applying the mass casualty plan. All the efforts made in the past months, the triage training, crowd control, hospital incident command system and the drill had started to pay off. Not one patient, from either the gangs or the police, died. Four critically injured patients received immediate surgery, 12 moderately injured patients were hospitalised for further care, and 15 'walking wounded' were discharged after stabilisation of their injuries.

After the incident, I interviewed nurses, doctors, trainees, security personnel, ancillary staff, and management involved in the incident, and most of them recognised that something was different this time. Teamwork improved as triage staff looked for the critically ill but salvageable patients, coordination amongst triage and treatment areas was enhanced, communication between leadership and the operational team was better, and security reinforced the emergency department's access points to achieve crowd control and patient flow.

That's when I finally understood that the coffee that I had enjoyed that morning was not just a regular one. It was a unique cup of Honduran coffee symbolising all the bitterness of being away from home, the sours of the long working hours, and the sweetness of having improved the emergency response in the country.

Now I'm departing on a new mission with another 3 kilograms of coffee, but also a broader perspective. I am more open-minded about what I can achieve and learn from the places I go to. •

A train at sunset in
Colombo, Sri Lanka.

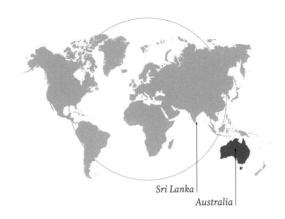

Sri Lanka

Australia

Tsunami to triage

HARENDRA COORAY

Harendra Cooray is an emergency physician at the Lady Ridgeway Hospital for Children in Colombo. He is Immediate Past President of the Sri Lanka College of Emergency Physicians.

Empty cans of Lion Lager and the remnants of festive chatter marked the end of another fun-filled Cooray-Bopearatchy family Christmas dinner. To allow my senses to recover from a night of merriment and spicy Sri Lankan food, Boxing Day of 2004 was to be a lazy-stay-at-home affair.

All that changed, however, when we heard about a strange phenomenon taking place along the eastern and southern coastlines. Our island nation's pristine beaches were extending out into the blue Indian Ocean as far as the eye could see, leaving locals and tourists bewildered. The events that occurred over the following hours, days and weeks were unimaginable, indescribable – and altogether unbearable.

A series of destructive waves was heading in our direction, fuelled by a devastatingly strong current. The human toll of the tsunami was immense. Approximately 31,299 people died and 21,411 were injured. More than 4000 people were reported missing and 1.5 million became displaced.

The destruction experienced by Sri Lanka was second only to Indonesia.

Our well-structured, free healthcare system was completely overwhelmed by this humanitarian disaster. Hospitals were in chaos. Patients flooded in from all directions – some with immediate life-threatening conditions, others simply disoriented by separation from their loved ones.

The absence of an emergency department to sort these patients meant that hundreds succumbed to their injuries due to a lack of timely assessment and treatment. Many others were stranded and unable to be retrieved to healthcare facilities. I often think of the lives that could have been saved if capacity to provide efficient emergency care had existed.

Emergency medicine was established in the United States of America following events that unfolded on 22 November 1963 at the Parkland Memorial Hospital in Dallas. An anaesthesiologist, a surgeon, a neurosurgeon, a physician and a cardiologist tried desperately to save the life of the critically injured President John F Kennedy. Despite their individual capabilities, none possessed the unique and comprehensive skill set of an emergency physician. For similar reasons, 26 December 2004 will possibly be remembered as the day emergency medicine was deemed an essential discipline in Sri Lanka.

The SSCCEM worked tirelessly to train specialists in a discipline that was non-existent. Many stood in the way of progress, but a few individuals refused to be deterred.

Strength in recovery

Sri Lanka's emergency medicine journey had been initiated two years earlier, when a group of broad-minded clinicians comprising anaesthesiologists, physicians, surgeons, paediatricians, cardiologists and obstetricians formed The Sri Lanka Society for Critical Care and Emergency Medicine (SSCCEM). Its goal was to establish and promote intensive care and emergency medicine as specialties, and to provide better care for critically ill patients.

The SSCCEM worked tirelessly to train specialists in a discipline that was non-existent. Many stood in the way of progress, but a few individuals refused to be deterred. They reached out to established international emergency medicine organisations for help and, after the events of Boxing Day 2004, these relationships proved critical.

Sri Lanka worked hard to rebuild and recover from the devastation

ABOVE: Concrete ruins of a house damaged by the tsunami on the eastern coast of Sri Lanka on Boxing Day 2004.

of the tsunami. Families that had lost everything – loved ones, and all their worldly possessions – were recovering from their grief. The outpouring of support from within and outside our paradise isle was overwhelming. International celebrities and sports stars from Oprah Winfrey to Shane Warne extended their generous support.

The southern coastline paid dearly, in terms of both lives and properties lost. This prompted the establishment of the Health for the South Project in 2008. The Sri Lankan Ministry of Health, the Karapitiya Teaching Hospital in Galle and the Victorian Government in Australia initiated an ambitious project to construct a fully equipped and staffed emergency trauma centre. Emergency medicine specialists from Melbourne's Alfred Hospital shared knowledge and skills with Sri Lankan doctors, nurses and administrators in an effort to build capacity to improve trauma care, triage and disaster response. The Karapitiya Teaching Hospital quickly became a symbol of progress in the face of adversity.

A personal journey
My own career story is intertwined with emergency medicine's growth in the wake of the tsunami. By 2008, I had completed 12 years of service

as a doctor. My wife, Therika, and I were the joyful parents of three adorable daughters aged seven, five and one. Having worked for many years in anaesthesia, it seemed the most obvious choice for specialist training for me.

This all changed one day after I had completed a very stressful paediatric surgical list. My supervising consultant inquired whether I would consider enrolling in a new post-graduate training course in critical care medicine. I gave it serious consideration because the events of Boxing Day 2004 had given me insight into the potential value of critical care in Sri Lanka. There was no doubt in my mind that the absence of emergency medicine and intensive care specialists led to many preventable deaths that day.

I was worried about enrolling in the program because I had very limited experience in intensive care. Nevertheless, I took up the challenge, completed my training and was among the first in Sri Lanka to obtain the Postgraduate Diploma in Critical Care Medicine. My career took an unexpected turn in 2010 when I joined SSCCEM and worked with colleagues to establish a specialist training course in intensive care. Unfortunately, the timing was not right, and the training program stalled

ABOVE: Some of Sri Lanka's first emergency medicine specialists pictured with emergency medicine luminary Judith Tintinalli (centre) at the 2019 International Conference on Emergency Medicine in Seoul, South Korea.

at diploma level; the planned extension to a doctorate qualification did not occur, and graduates were unable to achieve recognition as specialists. Along with many of my colleagues, I was left in the lurch.

This setback aside, the enthusiasm for establishing a critical care specialty continued and, by 2013, the undeterred efforts of many led to the establishment of a specialty training program in emergency medicine. I was inspired by those pioneers who had led the way and again decided to take a leap of faith, entering this new program with the first group of enthusiastic (and naive) trainees. After further training and study, I finally reached my goal and became one of Sri Lanka's first emergency medicine specialists. Little did I know that more challenges lay ahead.

The responsibility and sheer uncertainty of establishing a new specialty fell to a group of 16 of us. The only glimpse and experience we had of a truly functional state-of-the-art emergency department was following a week-long training visit to Singapore. Together we could see the endless possibilities that lay ahead to develop emergency departments that were as efficient and patient-centred as those in Singapore. We arrived home filled with excitement and the knowledge that there was a lot of work ahead.

> " I was inspired by those pioneers who had led the way and again decided to take a leap of faith, entering this new program with the first group of enthusiastic (and naive) trainees.

Fortune in disaster

The story of emergency medicine's development in Sri Lanka is punctuated by the disasters that catalysed progress. A decade on from the tsunami, the next event that changed the course of our journey took place in Nepal in April 2015.

The devastating earthquake that rocked that country also scuttled the plans of an Australian physician eager to share knowledge, skills and passion with receptive emergency medicine novices in Kathmandu. Nicholas Taylor, a senior specialist emergency physician from Canberra Hospital in Australia, had been granted six months' sabbatical leave to assist with emergency care development in Nepal. As a consequence of the earthquake, however, Dr Taylor and his family had to change plans: instead of relocating to Kathmandu, they arrived in Karapitiya.

We relished Dr Taylor's professionalism, commitment and passion, and he filled us with enthusiasm to develop emergency medicine in our country. His contribution to local teaching was critical because we had no emergency physicians in Sri Lanka to emulate. Dr Taylor's presence just prior to our emergency medicine exit exam in August 2016 was of enormous value.

By the end of that year, we had overcome many obstacles to complete our training in a specialty that did not previously exist in our country. The first group of successful post-doctorate emergency medicine graduates of Sri Lanka was born. As if to reward us for our success at the exit exam, an Australian-based international conference, Developing Emergency Medicine, hosted one of the biggest global gatherings of emergency physicians in Colombo.

We pinched ourselves to be sure it was not a dream. Workshops were conducted by emergency medicine luminaries, and clinicians from all over the world contributed to the discussions. The event was remarkable, but standing in front of the podium in the Grand Ballroom of the Galle Face Hotel, looking out at our entire emergency medicine community of trainees, trainers and dear friends from far-off lands, was truly the jewel in the crown.

> Now that I am back at home working as an emergency physician, not a day goes by without me reflecting upon an experience from Canberra and sharing it with my colleagues.

Global experience

As a final requirement of our specialty training, we needed to work overseas in an established emergency department for at least a year. Six of us from the first group of trainees made the long journey to the quiet, planned streets and freezing winter air of Canberra, Australia, to work in Canberra Hospital's modern emergency department. This was the first time I had been away from my wife and daughters.

The two years in Canberra were tough. Coming home to an empty, quiet apartment was never a pleasant experience, but I did enjoy the work with the friendly and supportive emergency department staff. Care was patient-centred, services were efficient, teamwork was impeccable, supervision was focused, communication was clear, teaching was engaging, and patients were so patient. Now that I am back at home working as an emergency physician, not a day goes by without me reflecting upon an experience from Canberra and sharing it with my colleagues.

Looking to the future

Seventeen years after the devastating tsunami, Sri Lanka has more than 20 specialist emergency physicians working in every corner of our island,

ABOVE: A boat washed up on the Sri Lankan coastline following the tsunami.

a growing specialist emergency training program with more than 200 trainees, and a college with a vision to improve efficiency and patient-centred care. Other disasters have challenged us – the Easter Sunday bombings and the COVID-19 pandemic among them – but we continue to learn and grow.

The journey from tsunami to triage has been a roller coaster ride. I have encountered many lows, but I remain focused on reaching further highs. Many people have inspired me, guided me, shared knowledge and skills with me, and supported me. I thank them all. •

ACKNOWLEDGEMENTS
I would like to thank the late (Mrs) Neelika Karunaratne, Chula Goonasekera, Sri Lal de Silva, Shane Curran, Jacqui Irvine, Sue Ieraci, Michael Downes, Dushan Jayaweera, Nilantha Lenora, Rahul Goswami, Dave Lamond, and Nicholas Taylor from the bottom of my heart. They have helped to make me a confident and compassionate emergency physician. Ayubowan.

Residential streets of Benghazi, 2020. People in societies affected by conflict are exposed to structural building risks, often long after active shelling has ceased.

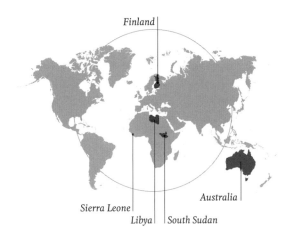

Finland

Sierra Leone

Australia

Libya | South Sudan

Global emergency care in conflict: a life and philosophy of health

AMY NEILSON

Amy Neilson is an Australian-trained rural generalist (emergency medicine) who works in humanitarian and conflict medicine with the International Committee of the Red Cross and Médecins Sans Frontières. She lives on an island in Tasmania.

I am typing from an apartment in Lapland. I close the windows not against the cold of the impending arctic winter, but rather the roadworks in the street. The stench and sound of pollution in this would-be pristine place are abrasive.

My teenage niece messages me on Instagram: 'It's so crazy to think you're on the other side of the globe; everything is so different, yet it's the same world'.

My eight-year-old niece FaceTimes me from Australia: 'I've been trying to call you all day', she rolls her eyes. Time zones are not yet of her comprehension. She dismisses my explanation that her day is my night. 'When are you coming home?', she implores.

People skate down the street, feet together, knees bent, propelled by poles. I watch fascinated. On wheels, they are preparing their bodies for the snow.

I am typing from an apartment in Lapland because I cannot get home.

I am writing to tell you of global emergency medical care through a particular frame, though a lens I've developed at some rough edges of our world.

Risks and borders

I am an Australian-trained rural and remote emergency medicine doctor who works in conflict and humanitarian medicine. I trained with the Australian College of Rural and Remote Medicine, obtaining a fellowship with Advanced Specialised Training in Emergency Medicine, while concomitantly pursuing a fellowship of the Australasian College of Tropical Medicine. I have worked on the consultant roster of large regional emergency departments, and in remote solo-doctor towns. To work overseas before having substantive skills to offer was not for me. I waited. It is hubris enough to go at all.

> To work in cultures other than our own is to take risks. There are risks to our health, risks to our lives, and risks to our freedoms. There are risks to those whom we hope to serve.

To work in cultures other than our own is to take risks. There are risks to our health, risks to our lives, and risks to our freedoms. There are risks to those whom we hope to serve. For surely, we do not imagine we impose ourselves upon those of another culture without at least some adverse effect. Humanitarianism is a worthy pursuit, but it can scarcely be disentangled from the history and present of colonialism.

My first position in global humanitarian work was in the 2014-2015 West African Ebola outbreak. It took some time to arrange leave from my regional Australian position. I was itchy to go. I stared at the news. 'If not me then who?' ran through my mind.

Risk became lived experience early into my position in Sierra Leone. I was exposed to the virus and was to be evacuated with two other international colleagues. My colleagues went home. I did not go home. The country of my birth denied me entry and I was granted admission instead to Switzerland - fittingly, the home of the Western humanitarian tradition.

I'd come up against a border. Borders have framed my understanding of our world - from Australia's reaction to the Norwegian shipping vessel *MV Tampa* to the creation of Australian Border Force, from my first

ABOVE: An Ebola warning sign in Central Africa.

displacement during the Ebola outbreak, through a continued career sans frontières to this moment, unable to return home from a position in Libya due to Australia's chosen response to the global COVID-19 pandemic. Instead of being home, I pause, and type from Lapland.

During 2020, Australia's escalation of flight caps excluded tens of thousands of citizens and permanent residents from their home. My contract had ended, and a member of my family had died. I needed to go home. The International Committee of the Red Cross could – it seemed – get me into any country bar the one in which I held citizenship. I paused in Europe. I extended my time in Libya. I supported a project in Jordan. All in all, I moved through nine countries; waiting. Australia's borders were extreme. I know of no other country whose response to the COVID-19 pandemic included the structural exclusion of its own citizens.

Conflict and health

I went on from the Ebola outbreak to work in Tripoli, northern Lebanon with refugees from Syria, in the long-standing Palestinian refugee camps of Bourj el-Barajneh and Chatilla, in the contested area of Abyei between South Sudan and Sudan during a time of increased fighting in the South

Sudanese civil war, in northern Syria during active conflict, to Mosul, Iraq for a period of post-conflict and an election, to Ukraine – training the trainers of resuscitative care during active conflict in the Luhansk region, back to South Sudan, and then on to Libya – the most complicated contest I've sought to appreciate yet.

Each job has been about the delivery of healthcare – in particular emergency medical care – to populations affected by conflict. My roles combine management, teaching, and the provision of clinical care, structured within organisations that seek to enable access to care via principled humanitarian action and the legal framework of the Geneva Conventions and their Additional Protocols. The principles of humanitarian action core to this tradition are neutrality, impartiality, humanity and independence.

The delivery of healthcare in conflict includes, but is not limited to, negotiating access to spaces in which people can safely access healthcare, assessing the security of facilities – not just for protection from the effect of munitions, but to be sure of the water supply, that the generator works and there is an emergency exit in a fire. It is stocking facilities with equipment to save lives and improve health, and it is training local care providers to use said equipment and consumables to deliver the best available quality care.

The delivery of healthcare in conflict involves potential retrieval systems, for it may be feasible to have only a foundational level of care close to a contact line. Healthcare is a powerful pull factor and you must exercise caution where you invite civilians to come. Working in conflict means working with multidisciplinary teams of engineers, lawyers, translators, weapons experts, economists and administrators of many forms. It is the lightest footprint of international staff and the highest quality of care. The best doctor will be local, and your value will be in extending their opportunities for continuing medical education within a broader system for negotiated safe access to care.

The registrar

The registrar is a colleague. She is an Australian-trained, experienced provider of global emergency care. I know her to be compassionate, skilled, careful and earnest.

She texts me from West Africa.

She describes children dying. She challenges her presence in that place. She describes a milieu of distress, frustration, effort and impact. She locates her experience amidst jobs gone by and wonders – as should we all – at how and why we do what we do. She lists the diseases she is seeing with greatest prevalence.

> **"**
> **Working in conflict means working with multidisciplinary teams of engineers, lawyers, translators, weapons experts, economists and administrators of many forms.**

'Cripes,' I reply, 'you are living in my memories'.

The clinical scenarios she describes transport me to South Sudan, five years ago, when I was immersed day and night in the life of a remote hospital. I'd not known before such endless resuscitative need. Malnutrition, sepsis, indeed malnourished sepsis, complicated malaria, tuberculosis, snake bite, pneumonia, meningitis, kala azar, eclampsia, burns, infected bullet wounds, and many presentations that would never be differentiated. I reel at the memories.

'There was a power outage', she messages me again, and goes on to describe the devastating sequelae to those dependent on oxygen.

I am back in the tuberculosis tent. I am running through the rain at night carrying a person all of my age and none of my weight to a room with power, shouting at a colleague to bring the oxygen concentrator.

'What's the back-up power situation?', I ask the registrar. How are we still here, I think? How far have we not come?

She texts again, 'The child survived the night, but they need a paediatric intensive care unit'.

I remember a child I once fought harder to save than anyone around me thought sensible. I remember painting myself into a corner, delivering paediatric intensive care in one of the most abused and forgotten corners of this blessed sweet earth.

She goes on. We discuss in some depth. And with her signature precision she concludes: 'None of the rules apply anymore'.

How do we respond when for all the energy, for even our measurable impacts, we perceive so very much stays the same? Maybe it even gets worse. How do we address our own impotence? It's the greatest and most terrible question for all who witness suffering - which is of course, in some measure, all who live.

The classical frame of humanitarianism is alive and dead. It is necessary, and it is inadequate. It serves, and it harms. Were it a game, we would not be winning. I suggest we stay standing with honest contemplation and a broader, deeper lens; with re-prosecution of both method and frame. We need this now with some urgency.

> Our perception of need in places other than our own must stem from an appreciation of complexity and a position of humility regarding our self and our traditions.

The other

This is a reflection upon borders. Why? Because borders and 'the other' are a frame for the complexity of the work of healthcare in conflict.

We cannot separate the climate emergency from a myriad of global conflicts. We cannot position ourselves as a rescuer, or an imparter of skills and value without acknowledging our role in harm caused. We better appreciate 'the other' and understand exclusion when we become 'othered' ourselves.

To reflect upon the culture and responses of our homes is to firm our understanding of health as a political entity. Our perception of need in places other than our own must stem from an appreciation of complexity and a position of humility regarding our self and our traditions. Borders are intrinsic to the matter of governance, for you do not govern an unknown expanse. And the human experience of health is in some manner at all times embedded in the experience of government. What is the citizen, what is the state, and where do the responsibilities and rights of each rest their heads with certainty?

Personal, philosophical and ethical reflection is paramount to the delivery of healthcare at the edges of humanity if we seek something akin to humility. Our humanity soars as the space between ourselves and the other disappears.

The emergency

Everything is so different, yet it's the same world, my niece said to me.

I came to the Arctic because I am drawn to extremes. The world reveals herself to us at her edges. She is plainer to see. I came to the Arctic because I know we are losing her. The diesel fumes remind me viscerally of the climate emergency. The building shakes as workmen drill the concrete, and I wonder for the nth time how much our world can take.

I take it as given that there is a nexus between conflict, the climate emergency and human migration; a nexus driven by choices of governments that maps its outcomes to the human experience of health. Our planet is dying and us with it. I say us, because I am not interested in the perception of those who see heat, illness, conflict or drought as belonging to those unfortunate people 'over there'. They are us. And we would be wise to rely on inductive reasoning as we seek to map global urgent care.

The invitation is to witness, someone dear once said to me. It is. And as we witness, we bear responsibility to act. I have long believed that the practice of medicine in the humanitarian sector requires seeing both the wood and the trees. I've watched colleagues who've known only privileged, wealthy systems learn this in the COVID-19 pandemic – there is no perfect answer to the needs of both the population and the one whom someone holds dear. The responsibility is to acknowledge the broader tensions and to act.

And so too it is with the climate emergency. As privileged providers of emergency care we bear responsibility for our contribution to those affected by air quality, by pandemic and by weather-related shock events. We seek to improve access to health globally, as indeed we should, and we must. Equally, we are responsible for acknowledging the depth of our own privilege and the forces of governance that impair the health of our own selves and of those we seek to serve.

Health is paramount, it is precious, it is personal, and it is political – global or local, no more, no less. May we find our place within. ●

PART 3

INSPIRING INDIVIDUALS

Profiles of clinicians who are leading change in their communities

Phillip Kampai (left) and George Jack (right) are paramedics with ProMedical Vanuatu in Port Vila, Vanuatu.

The Blue Lagoon near
Port Vila, Efate, Vanuatu.

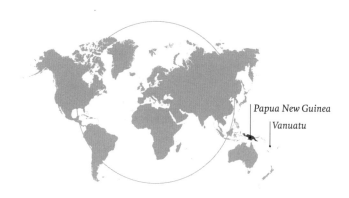

Papua New Guinea

Vanuatu

Brooms, mops and cookie jars

VINCENT ATUA

Vincent Atua is the sole emergency physician at Vila Central Hospital in Port Vila, Vanuatu. He was one of the first graduates of the emergency medicine specialty training program in Papua New Guinea.

The phone call came out of the blue. It was 2018 and I was at home in Madang, on the north coast of Papua New Guinea's main island. It was a former colleague calling, from Townsville in Australia. He asked if I would like to go to Vanuatu to work. 'It's a locum job', he said. 'They need someone with your experience to help start the new emergency department in Port Vila.' The Vanuatu Ministry of Health had identified the need for a well-functioning emergency department led by an emergency physician and had been looking for a suitable person for several months.

At the time, I was the medical director of Modilon Hospital, the provincial referral centre, and the only emergency physician in Madang. Luckily, one of my former trainees had just passed his specialist exams and was eager to take over as emergency department director. Even though I had a succession plan in place, moving to Vanuatu would be a major decision.

I had worked as an emergency physician in Papua New Guinea for 10 years, and a shift to Port Vila would mean leaving my comfort zone and my network of friends and colleagues. I wondered what my wife would think. Unarguably, it would be a good opportunity to earn extra money and pay off the mortgage a bit more quickly ...

An exciting adventure

On Boxing Day that year, I flew with my family to Vanuatu to start my new role as the first full-time emergency physician at Vila Central Hospital. It was an exciting proposition to establish the new emergency department and start a training pathway in emergency medicine. Supporting Ni-Vanuatu doctors to become emergency medicine specialists would allow them to eventually take the lead and chart their own course in emergency care.

The emergency department had been run by nurses for as long as the hospital had been in existence, with non-specialist doctors and the occasional ad hoc volunteer providing short-term support. While the nurses were doing the best that they could, it was clear to the rest of the hospital that the department needed senior clinical oversight to realise its potential.

I arrived with big dreams and much excitement, but I accepted that it would be a challenge to start a department from scratch in a foreign country.

Other core specialties, such as internal medicine and obstetrics and gynaecology, were becoming established by the first batch of indigenous specialists, all of whom had trained in neighbouring Fiji. There was general agreement that the emergency department needed specialist medical leadership, alongside a range of other improvements.

A report had been written by an emergency physician from Aotearoa New Zealand, funded by the New Zealand Ministry of Foreign Affairs and Trade, who had previously worked in Vanuatu. This provided the framework for reform. The emergency department lacked basic components, such as triage, standard operating procedures and data-collection processes, not to mention a shortage of capacity in research and education. I arrived with big dreams and much excitement, but I accepted that it would be a challenge to start a department from scratch in a foreign country.

This story serves as a poignant reminder of the early days in the emergency department. I was the only doctor and worked 18-hour days, seven days a week, carrying a huge clinical burden. I faced the daunting task

ABOVE: Emergency physician Vincent Atua teaching a primary trauma care course alongside Australian volunteer Libby White. Libby was one of a small number of Australian volunteers with critical skills who worked in Vanuatu to support local organisations through the pandemic in 2021.

of introducing change and convincing the staff to break from traditional ways of doing things. I wanted their support to improve patient care, but also to bring about a paradigm shift in work ethic and culture. These are my reflections of the experience, and the accidental occasions that helped to convert an old 'casualty ward' to a modern emergency department.

The mop

The hospital was short on cleaning staff, and we were only able to get a cleaner once a day. The most practical time to clean the department was early in the morning when most of the patients had gone. The floors could then be mopped with some guarantee that they wouldn't be immediately soiled by mud-laden footwear.

Frequently, the few nurses on each shift were so overwhelmed with demands for patient care that they couldn't stop to do the cleaning. To do so would have attracted the ire of the frustrated patients in the waiting room.

Among other factors, the lack of cleanliness caused the department to appear disorganised and chaotic. I had no idea who was coming in and out, who needed my attention first, or where to find equipment. Plus, it was not good for infection prevention and control.

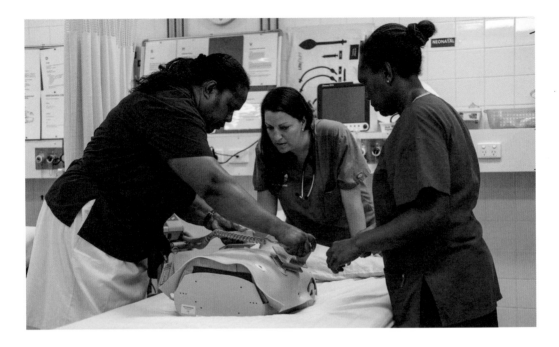

One day, after whingeing about the general cleanliness of the place, I picked up a broom and started sweeping. I then mopped the floors and emptied the waste bins. I helped the nurses make beds and, instead of waiting for porters, started pushing patients to the radiology department or the wards as the need arose. I did this without fuss, and out of necessity. Plus, I wanted to play my role as a team member.

This behaviour came as quite a shock to the staff and patients. It's not often that you see or hear of the emergency physician, or any consultant for that matter, sweeping floors in his or her department. The nurses were embarrassed and spurred into action. Other support staff, such as the drivers, porters and clerks, also began to give 'the boss' a hand with the cleaning when they had a spare moment.

Over time, I no longer had to do the cleaning regularly as the staff would already have done it. Sometimes, patients' carers and guardians would even offer to help sweep the floor after seeing me with a broom. I welcomed their contribution and encouraged it, because it allowed them to do their little bit to help their hospital.

Somehow, keeping the department clean had a calming effect on the place. The simple but necessary act of picking up a mop was seen as

ABOVE: Emergency nurse Roselyn Morribo (left), nurse aid Adenise Meltemal (right) and Australian volunteer Dani Clark (centre) at Vila Central Hospital, Vanuatu. Dani was supported by the Australian Volunteers Program to volunteer as an emergency response trainee with the Vila Central Hospital in 2020.

a sign of humility. I rapidly gained the respect and admiration of my staff. It was only then that I felt qualified to lead them and institute change.

Cookie jars and sausage sizzles

Initially, there were no proper handovers at the end of each shift. One of the first things I did was request a whiteboard from hospital management. We used it as a tracking board to monitor patients' whereabouts in the department and document their care plans, so that I had some oversight of what was happening. It also meant critically ill patients were not being missed amid the chaos of a busy emergency department. The whiteboard became the gathering point for shift handovers and ward meetings and gave us a sense of control.

One of my trainees suggested a cookie jar as a way of encouraging engagement with the tracking board. We asked the staff to fill it up every morning with cookies as a way of creating a focal point for conversations, fostering collegiality and promoting teamwork in the department staff room. Bringing some order to the space was essential. At the time, the tearoom also functioned as the emergency department reception, triage window, switchboard, ambulance driver's station and departmental office. That novel idea did just the trick, and the cookie jar remains today. It's a reminder of how a simple gesture can achieve so much.

> " That novel idea did just the trick, and the cookie jar remains today. It's a reminder of how a simple gesture can achieve so much.

The hospital did not allocate a budget for replacement parts and the small-but-essential items that are required in the emergency department. The absence of these items, such as pillows and weighing scales, hugely impacted our work. To raise the necessary funds, I started arranging sausage sizzles – a simple stall selling barbecued meat to passers-by. Over time, many sausages bought many pillows, as well as a triage desk, lockers for the staff and some new furniture.

I also started networking with people in the business community to get support for the department. Seats for the waiting area were donated by a local bank and small grants helped to renovate our new staff tearoom, which also doubles as a teaching space. I discovered underutilised sources of funding within the Ministry of Health and its partners and enlisted their support. We eventually organised a hospital ball and raised funds for equipment and other improvements.

I am still involved in organising the annual hospital ball, but the proceeds now go to other sections of the hospital - the most recent being the children's ward. I have discovered a lot of goodwill in the community, particularly directed towards the hospital, but have learned that a lot of social and professional networking is required to harness these resources.

Waiting room woes

Port Vila, like many other Pacific Islands, doesn't have a system of after-hours clinics that provide public primary care. Hence, after the sun sets, the only option for unwell patients is to attend the emergency department. Overcrowding in the waiting room is common, as is frustration with the perceived lack of timely attention.

In those early days, there was no triage system, no reception desk and no means to inform patients about the prioritisation process. Patients requiring admission needed review by an inpatient doctor prior to transfer to the ward and incurred long waiting times. This led to chronic access block (delays in the admission of inpatients to hospital beds), exacerbating the overcrowding.

The process has taught me that humility, and sometimes humour, are the better ways to lead change, especially in a different cultural environment from your own.

The emergency department was an open space with a section nearest the door designated as a 'waiting room'. It was not physically separate and would be more appropriately described as a 'waiting space'.

We couldn't hide from the prying eyes. We worked frantically to clear the waiting room, attend to the critically ill and somehow still appear in control amid the chaos and frequent interruptions. Many of these came from concerned family and patients' guardians, asking, 'When will we be seen by the nurse?' or 'Can you see my child first?'

Several programs are helping to address these challenges. An established partnership with the Aotearoa New Zealand Medical Treatment Scheme was able to fund two intensive, nurse-run, three-week short courses for all emergency department nurses at Vila Central Hospital and a group from the outer islands.

The course, accredited by the Australian College of Emergency Nursing, has provided a solid and uniform platform for all the nursing staff in the department. Its delivery also coincided with the arrival of our first Australian nurse educator volunteer, who helped gel the culture of emergency nursing in our staff, allowing them to appreciate their crucial role in the team. The two volunteers who followed have contributed immensely to the improvements in nursing in the emergency department and have had a hospital-wide impact.

In 2020, a collaboration with the Australian Volunteers Program, an Australian Government-funded initiative, and ACEM provided the opportunity for visiting emergency medicine trainees from Australia to work with us for three to six months. Additionally, international visitors and collaborators have helped us grow as a department in the last three years, with progress slowed only by the impact of COVID-19 on international travel.

Of particular benefit has been the establishment of a new triage system. This has not only improved our processes, but also our data collection and analysis. I now have four full-time Ni-Vanuatu trainees who are undertaking the ACEM certificate (a basic training program in emergency care) and are set to commence advanced training in emergency medicine in the next two years. The combination of these improvements has had a substantial impact on the waiting room and beyond.

Onwards and upwards
The emergency department in Port Vila has grown in leaps and bounds since the days that I was mopping floors. Some changes were easy, but others have required the sustained involvement of staff over a long period of time.

I've learned that it's important to celebrate the wins, but also to comfort one another over the losses. The process has taught me that humility, and sometimes humour, are the better ways to lead change, especially in a different cultural environment from your own.

I'm glad I answered the phone that day. ●

ACKNOWLEDGEMENTS
Support for the visiting Australian nurses and emergency medicine trainees is provided by the Australian Volunteers Program, an Australian Government–funded initiative managed by AVI in a consortium with Cardno and Alinea Whitelum.

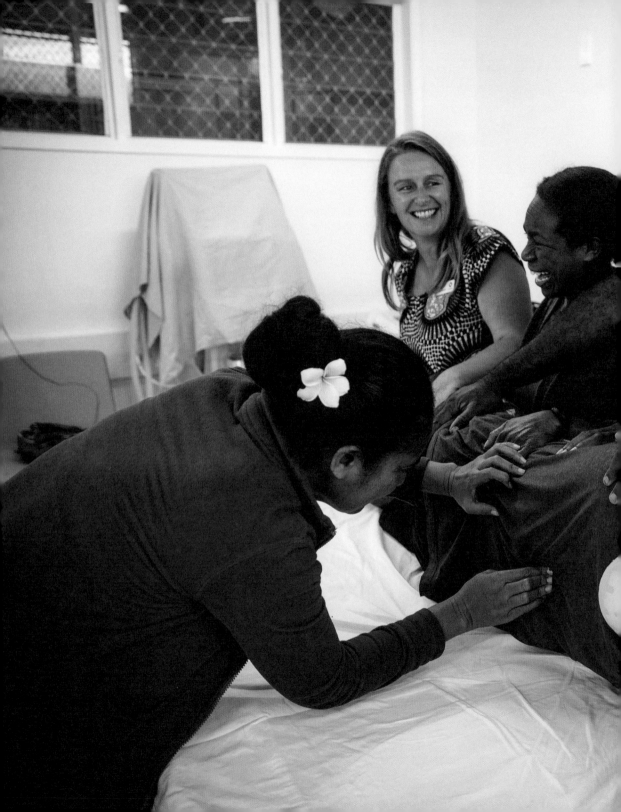

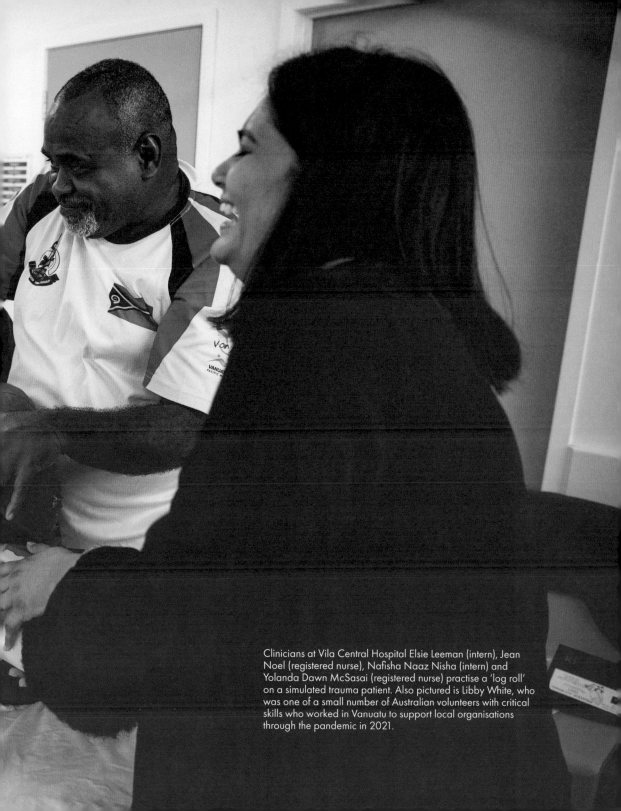

Clinicians at Vila Central Hospital Elsie Leeman (intern), Jean Noel (registered nurse), Nafisha Naaz Nisha (intern) and Yolanda Dawn McSasai (registered nurse) practise a 'log roll' on a simulated trauma patient. Also pictured is Libby White, who was one of a small number of Australian volunteers with critical skills who worked in Vanuatu to support local organisations through the pandemic in 2021.

Ankole cattle in Lake
Mburo National Park
near Mbarara, Uganda.

Uganda

A pioneer's perspective

JUSTINE ATHIENO ODAKHA

Justine Odakha is one of the first graduates of emergency medicine in Uganda. She is an emergency physician at Mbarara Regional Hospital and an assistant lecturer of emergency medicine at Mbarara University of Science and Technology in southwest Uganda.

It was the start of 2017 and I had just handed in my resignation letter. My luggage was in the car boot, the engine was roaring, and the trees were rushing past me. *All Things New* by Hillsong was playing on my car radio. It should have been an exhilarating moment, but I could still hear the doubting voices of my friends and mentors. 'What is emergency medicine?' 'Is it even being offered in Uganda? It will be very hard for you to get a job.'

I was leaving the best place I had ever worked – a 250-bed community hospital in Kiwoko in Central Uganda – on a path that some had called career suicide. I was on my way to start a traineeship 300 kilometres away in a specialty that wasn't yet recognised in the country. Why did I have such zeal to take a leap into the unknown?

And then I remembered the moment in the second year of my general practice that I met a young patient named Mary. The day she arrived at our emergency room door changed my life. And I know we saved hers.

The ward round that day had been smooth, and the team was steadily arranging discharges when we were all startled by a loud cry for help at the emergency room door. Mary, newly married, had suddenly lost consciousness while having breakfast with her husband. He wasted no time rushing her to the hospital and I looked up as she was wheeled through the emergency room doors.

She was restless as she lay on her trolley; her skin was sweaty, and she was breathing quickly. After a thorough history was taken and an examination, it became clear that Mary had anaemia and abdominal tenderness. She was rapidly losing consciousness. It appeared she had been bleeding in the abdomen, from either her upper gastrointestinal system or a ruptured ectopic pregnancy, for more than a few hours. However, without obvious clinical signs, bedside testing or a point-of-care ultrasound scan, there was limited capacity to establish the underlying pathology. Despite oxygen therapy and rapid IV fluids, Mary suddenly started gasping and needed assistance to breathe.

After a brief but difficult discussion with her family about her prognosis, I called the anaesthetist, who intubated Mary. We then referred her to an intensive care unit (ICU) in the capital city, Kampala, 60 kilometres away. Three days later Mary, accompanied by her husband, came back to thank my team for having given her another chance at life. She was diagnosed with a leaking ectopic pregnancy, which was repaired, and she spent two days in ICU before returning home.

> I was beginning to understand the significance of emergency medicine and it's impact on the people of Uganda.

Timely decisions

Our treatment of Mary - the intubation and ventilation - gave her enough time to get the necessary investigations and receive much-needed care. I wondered how many more Ugandans could use a few more minutes to give the clinical team enough time for investigations and definitive management.

Advanced diagnostics and critical care facilities are limited to Kampala, our capital city, and, in a country where patients seek medical care mostly when they are in advanced stages of medical need, how many could use an extra second? How many patients need someone with the right skills to help them linger a little longer on the edge between life and death before accessing an ICU?

ABOVE LEFT: Justine Odakha.

ABOVE RIGHT: Emergency department drugs.

As part of my medical learning, I often take notes highlighting for myself how patients had been saved, or died, and what could have been done better, or differently. I was beginning to understand the significance of emergency medicine and it's impact on the people of Uganda.

Mary's story had emphasised the importance of timely decisions. It was a metaphor for both medical care in my country and my career. I hoped my decision to take up a new challenge would be both timely and a good choice.

As I approached Mbarara, I was met by the refreshing winds of the countryside. The magnificent sun-kissed hills with meticulously arranged terraces made me feel serene and assured. I knew my next three years of training at Mbarara University of Science and Technology, with clinical work at the Mbarara Regional Referral Hospital, a 600-bed teaching facility in the nation's southwest, would be tumultuous and unpredictable. But I would have the beautiful natural environment around me to escape to when times became hard.

The traineeship in emergency medicine was even more challenging than I had anticipated, and those hills saw a great deal of me. My friends back home continued to question me and added to my own inner doubts.

Although the Ministry of Health, Mbarara University, and Mbarara Hospital had supported the launch of our program, few lecturers within the university and doctors within the hospital understood the concept of emergency medicine. Most thought it was a duplication of existing specialties. Each day was a battle of existence and a personal struggle to validate the value of emergency medicine.

Slowly the trainees in our program gained ground and our colleagues began to appreciate the value we brought to the management team. We began working with ECGs and as ultrasound technicians, but advanced to become the cardiac arrest team, and later we transformed into an emergency medicine response team. In my second year of training, after much negotiation, lobbying and training of hospital staff, we launched a triage system and streamlined the flow of emergency department patients. This provided an opportunity to showcase the importance of emergency medicine as the receiving teams often had little to do after a patient had gone through our hands.

My next career-defining patient arrived during the time that I and my fellow trainees had begun to manage patients firsthand. This was when I began to truly appreciate the specialty that I had signed up for.

Ntoroke was brought in with a lacerated throat, a transected windpipe and severed major neck vessels following an attack by thugs on his way home from work. He was bleeding profusely from his wounds and choking on the blood.

If I had encountered this patient before my first year of training, I doubt that I would have had the confidence to approach him. Thanks to our initial training, we knew to rush him to the resuscitation bay and insert a breathing tube down his windpipe through the open wound. By this time, he was in shock and confused and aggressive.

The bay became like a beehive, with the worker bees busy at what they do best. Each of us took on a role: one person managed the airway, another provided a pressure dressing to his neck wound, others administered drips, warmed fluids, took blood samples, or performed a bedside ultrasound, and one called the ENT (otorhinolaryngology) team.

The room became quiet only after the patient was in the operating theatre. However, what lingered on everyone's mind was, 'Was all this worth it?' The following morning, I was ecstatic to learn that Ntoroke had survived his terrible ordeal. I had never been more inspired, and I was ready to take on my next challenge.

Mbarara is known as the land of milk and honey. Its fields are usually littered with herds of hundreds of dramatically horned Ankole cattle and local traffic is often stopped as these gentle beasts cross the highways.

The men (they are always men) whose livelihoods depend on these cattle are frequently the subject of medical emergencies ranging from testicular torsion, caused by cattle kicks, to pesticide poisoning during the cattle dipping seasons.

My next patient was a cattle keeper who had attempted suicide using a tick-killing pesticide. When I first saw John, I thought he would become another one of our cardiac arrest statistics. He was unresponsive, deeply unconscious, with dilated unreactive pupils and a respiratory rate so shallow that we needed to squint to count it. We immediately prioritised assisting his breathing and gave him medication to reverse the overdose.

Had this been a high-income country, it is likely that the decision to insert a breathing tube into John's lungs to help him breathe might have come more easily than it did for us. The fact that this patient needed a ventilator, and that our three-bed ICU was already full, meant that he would have to remain in the emergency department for an extended period, even though we had barely half the required number of nurses. We would also have to support his breathing manually, because there was no ventilator in the department. After discussing the pros and cons, we decided to proceed and placed the breathing tube into his lungs. His breathing effort improved after a few hours and he was placed on the 'Harry T-piece', an improvised breathing device invented by one of our tutors from a saline bottle.

> "
> The men (they are always men) whose livelihoods depend on these cattle are frequently the subject of medical emergencies.

In the early hours of the morning, I was pleasantly surprised to find John awake and sipping a drink. He had woken up 12 hours after intubation and pulled the breathing tube out himself. This young man, who had been on the brink of death, lived not only to see another day but to tell stories of where he had been. Nothing could better validate my decision to practise emergency medicine. This was definitely my calling.

A vision realised

Four years after completing the three long years of training in Mbarara, I am now a specialist. As I stand by the resuscitation bay instructing a trainee to perform an ultrasound-guided procedure to numb a nerve for a patient with a broken leg, and seeing the excellent technique with which it is being executed, I feel a strong sense of accomplishment. The activities I see daily around the emergency department tell a story that

had once only been a dream. On one side of the department two boda boda (motorcyclist) patients from separate accidents are admitted, each has a severe head injury with expanding haematomas and they are both waiting for theatre space before decompressive surgery; while on the other side of the department another young man is admitted with organophosphate poisoning, intubated and awaiting an ICU bed; and a diabetic lady admitted with serious complications is receiving fluids and medications as the team struggles to keep her alive.

ABOVE: Boda boda (motorcycle taxis) are a popular form of transport in Uganda.

The role of emergency medicine is now quite well defined in Mbarara. Our colleagues actively refer critically ill patients to us, we receive referrals from surrounding health facilities and our consultation numbers have increased. Now, rather than trying to prove our importance, our concerns are more that we are an inadequate number to serve a growing need across the hospital. But the future is bright. More trainees are enrolling in emergency medicine. More medical, nursing and physiotherapy undergraduate students volunteer to be part of our team. More medical officers have been employed to work in the emergency department and clinicians' attitudes have changed - from futility to anything is possible and 'let's give him a chance'. The university now has enough emergency

> The fact that I'm not on the sidelines watching, but have been actively involved in this great journey of emergency medicine in Uganda, makes me feel like one of the chosen ones.

physicians for 24-hour coverage of its hospital emergency department, and more partners provide support to keep it running.

I have advocated for emergency medicine at every opportunity – at conferences, in stakeholder meetings with partners in emergency care and within the faculty, to clinicians and students at Mbarara Regional Referral Hospital and University. I have mentored colleagues at every opportunity. I have aimed to model a non-futility attitude and a fast-paced 'never-procrastinate without trying to treat' approach. I genuinely believe the teams I work with have recognised and responded to my approach to very sick patients and my zeal to do my best. I have intervened wherever possible when patients were deteriorating and encouraged medical trainees and students to do the same. I have taught first aid and emergency medicine principles to undergraduate students. I have been resilient and kept pushing for our speciality.

Although it is still a challenge to create an ideal emergency department, and we still grapple with theatre space, diagnostics and ICU space, there are many achievements to be celebrated. Uganda now boasts at least two comprehensive emergency medicine trainee programs. The one at Mbarara University of Science and Technology, where I now lecture in emergency medicine, is run by the emergency physicians who were in my class. There is another at Makerere University in Kampala and its first class of trainees is ready to graduate. Government scholarships are offered in emergency medicine and our specialty is at the centre of the country's COVID-19 response. With a National Emergency Care society, undergraduate emergency medicine interest groups in two universities, training programs for in-service in-hospital and pre-hospital emergency care, and a soon-to-be functional national call and dispatch centre, emergency medicine in Uganda is on an upward trajectory.

The fact that I'm not on the sidelines watching but have been actively involved in this great journey of emergency medicine in Uganda, makes me feel like one of the chosen ones. I'm proud to be a part of this great development, which has changed the face of healthcare in my country. •

Brasilia, the federal capital of Brazil, as seen from the city's TV Tower.

Brazil

Emergency medicine arrives in Brasília

JULE SANTOS

Jule Santos is an attending physician in the emergency department of the Santa Maria Regional Hospital in Brasília, Brazil. She is head of the emergency medicine trainee program and teacher at Medical School Uniplac, a member of the Brazilian Society of Emergency Medicine and founder of the medicine blog *emergenciarules.wpcomstaging.com*

Lately I have experienced a different kind of completeness: the sparkle in the eyes of emergency trainees as they witness their first patient survive a cardiac arrest without neurologic impairment. I feel pride in their joy as they receive acknowledegment from the patient, their family and the team.

One such patient, now extubated – three days after the trainees had performed 15-minutes of CPR – recognised and embraced their family. That moment was the first time in four years that I allowed myself to breathe a sigh of relief and think: yes, it's working. Our training program is working.

It is strange to consider that emergency medicine once did not exist in Brazil as a specialty, and that a group of people fought for more than 20 years to have it recognised. It took me a long time to become aware of the existence of this specialty, the one that would become my destiny.

The internet and social media were important for my development as an emergency physician, and for the growth of our residency program in Brasília. They provided a connection for the exchange of knowledge and experience, as well as kindness, which was essential to raise the profile of emergency medicine and inspire others to follow.

The power of free knowledge and its possibility of change is indescribable. A single article changed my life.

It was not until five years after I finished medical school that I became aware of emergency medicine as a specialty. I was finishing training in internal medicine, preparing to start a traineeship in cardiology, but feeling odd. Displaced and sad. Sad that I was about to leave so much behind; too many opportunities to treat other medical conditions. I was already committed to a career in cardiac emergency, but realised I would no longer help patients with strokes, diabetic ketoacidosis, sepsis …

I commented on this feeling of displacement to my preceptor, and he told me about an association named the Brazilian Society of Emergency Medicine (ABRAMEDE) formed by a group of doctors to fight for the recognition of this new specialty. The doctors were from the states of Rio Grande do Sul and Ceará and had founded a training program in emergency medicine. They had been fighting for its recognition for about 20 years. That day, when I got home, I researched everything I could on the internet about this new specialty: emergency medicine.

> The power of free knowledge and its possibility of change is indescribable. A single article changed my life.

Brave new world

I found a free translation of the article by the American emergency physician Joe Lex, in which he explained an emergency physician's work. That article opened up a new world for me. For the first time in my professional life, I felt that I belonged somewhere. I was sure. This was what I wanted to do for the rest of my career.

As soon as I finished my residency, I worked in the emergency department of a secondary hospital in my city. I saw many critically ill patients, but we were not a teaching hospital, and we had no educational support. I was afraid of not being able to keep up to date with good practice but, fortunately, I discovered Free Open Access Medical Education (FOAMed).

FOAMed brought me to the heart of emergency medicine and gave me the opportunity to meet amazing people. After reading Lex's article, I continued to look for more information about emergency medicine.

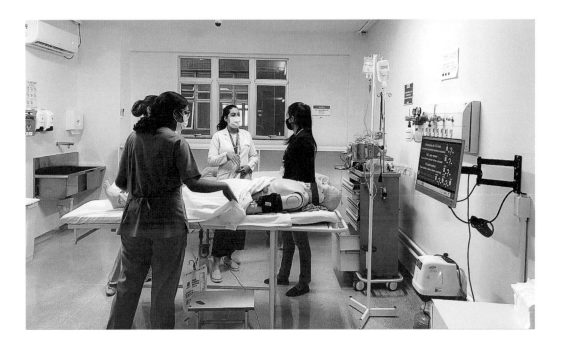

ABOVE: Brazilian emergency medicine trainees participate in simulation training.

I discovered the site emdocs.net, and it filled me with enthusiasm. This website offered educational material that had a context, history, and a clear thread between illness, treatment and practice, and was committed to evidence. I learned more about the history of emergency medicine, how residency programs worked in other countries, and a different way of teaching. I had never found anything like this in Portuguese.

FOAMed was created by emergency physicians. It is an initiative committed to the free dissemination of knowledge, without cost, focused on quality. Knowledge that aims to help new evidence reach the bedside faster, translating into better patient care.

But it did more than that for me. It taught me that there was an entire body of literature focused on emergency conditions. It offered more than just a cardiologist talking about how to treat a heart attack. Emergency physicians explained how to make a differential diagnosis of chest pain, about the main difficulties in diagnosing and starting treatment. It was information in line with my daily practice in the emergency room. I felt understood. I felt part of a group. And I felt inspired to do a better job.

I had to spread that knowledge. That's why I started my page emergenciarules.com.br

I wanted to talk about emergency medicine in the same way as FOAMed, with a focus on storytelling and quality evidence. I translated a lot of content into Portuguese, because the feeling of reading something interesting in your own language is priceless. Many people approach me telling me how they got to know about emergency medicine through my articles, or how they learned something new, and improved patient care. That feeling is the driving force that keeps me going.

Emergency medicine was finally recognised as a specialty in Brazil in 2015 and several residency programs started across the country. It was no longer a no-man's land, destined only for newly graduated doctors who would stay for a short period of their careers. It was its own practice, with its own literature and its own way of thinking.

Now, as I look back, I realise there were many moments when I was scared and wanted to give up; when I felt alone, unsupported, and often misunderstood.

But the interesting thing about emergency medicine is that, once recognised, the importance of this specialty for each hospital becomes very clear. When people stop to think, it seems irrational that they don't have doctors specialising in acute illness and critical conditions. The residency program had been approved in Brasília, and now it needed tutors. Experts from other areas were invited to help form a new specialty. As a specialist in internal medicine, studying emergency medicine and forming my own mindset, I was invited to take on the coordination of this new specialty. I am very grateful for the trust my colleagues placed in me.

Global connections

I accepted the challenge with great hope in my heart. And, in that first year, I began the task of learning to be an emergency physician, a preceptor for trainees and head of a residency program. I travelled the country and the world; I went to conferences, exchanged emails and tweets, asked for help from hospitals around the world where emergency medicine was already available, and I brought back so much knowledge, so much affection, advice, and a little bit of kindness from all of these people. They formed the foundation and provided the support I needed to help sustain our emergency trainee program.

I attended a conference organised by Females Working in Emergency Medicine (FemInEM) that took place in New York 2019 and here I met incredible and inspiring women, leaders, scientists and teachers with stories of overcoming difficulties. I spoke briefly with one emergency physician and education leader, who was interested in my posts on Twitter,

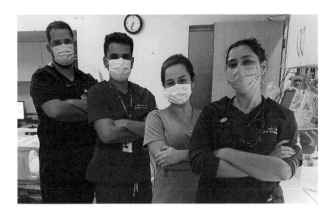

> **“**
> That's why I believe that knowledge is power, that it belongs to everyone and must be provided for free.

ABOVE: Jule (far right) and emergency medicine colleagues at Santa Maria Regional Hospital in Brasília.

during a break. I mentioned some of the difficulties we faced in our program, and she made a simple observation about leadership that deeply impacted me and changed my relationship with my trainees. She helped me overcome some of my insecurities and I firmly embraced my position as a leader. I don't think she knows how profoundly she affected me and what she did for the patients my trainees have saved and will save.

These days, I've been to many FOAMed-inspired conferences and taken airway and resuscitation courses. I've been to hospitals in Sydney, Boston, Toronto, Halifax and been welcomed by leaders and changemakers within emergency medicine education. I have been treated with respect and kindness. Importantly, I have seen that they practise the medicine they preach on social media, too.

I follow a relentless quest to be the best person I can be. I try to transmit that energy to my students and followers. I think of the possibility of impacting medical education and future generations of physicians in Brazil and beyond as a privilege and a great responsibility. I am so grateful for everyone who believed in me, encouraged me and contributed to my growth.

My story illustrates the importance of connecting, the importance of free knowledge and the things that can be achieved through them both.

The fact that a doctor in the interior of Brazil had access to content created by international experts and that, with the help of colleagues from Brazil, was able to build the foundations for a new specialty is inspiring. That's why I believe that knowledge is power, that it belongs to everyone and must be provided for free.

I believe that connection between people is essential for the exchange of experiences and to witness both possibilities and differences. It is what drives us towards the development of a better society, and ultimately, a better world. •

A remote beach in Kiribati.

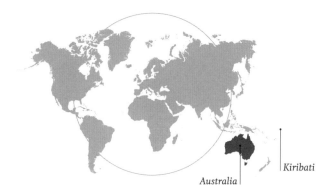

Australia | Kiribati

Short trip, long legacy

BRADY TASSICKER AND FATIMA MWEMWENIKEAKI

Brady Tassicker is an emergency physician based in Burnie in Tasmania.
He also works in Kiribati and other sites throughout the Pacific region.

Fatima Mwemwenikeaki is an i-Kiribati doctor. She works in the emergency
department at Tungaru Central Hospital on Tarawa Island in Kiribati.

Brady: My phone rang, cutting through the hubbub of voices in the bar, and drowning the buzz of mosquitoes. Excusing myself, I stepped out to take the call.

'Dr Brady, it's Dr Fatima. I'm in the emergency department. I need your help.'

After hearing the details of the case and providing some preliminary advice, I asked my colleague Jeremy if he wanted to come with me to the hospital. He nodded, and we commenced the 30-minute drive to Tungaru Central Hospital.

Fatima: I was on call at the emergency department at Tungaru Central Hospital. Between 8pm and 9pm, a lady of 50-plus years was brought in by ambulance, accompanied by her daughter. The lady had severe chest pain, more on the left side, heavy and tight in nature, radiating to her left arm, up to her neck and jaw. She was laid on the trolley, attended to by the nurses, given the medications that had been ordered and oxygen via mask. The pain had not subsided despite the medication and within a few minutes she collapsed.

Brady: Jeremy and I were part of an eight-person team, visiting Kiribati to teach the Emergency Life Support International (ELSi) course. The aim was to teach hospital staff a systematic approach to the management of critically unwell patients. The course had been developed in Australia but, at some point, was modified for use in Papua New Guinea. It has since been rolled out in multiple countries throughout the Asia-Pacific region.

The original Australian course no longer exists, but the international version continues to be taught across the region and is highly regarded. It consists of a series of modules, which can be added or subtracted based on local patterns of disease or injury. It is very hands-on, focusing on what can be done with locally available resources.

I knew Kiribati well. It was two years since I had finished a year-long stay, working in the emergency department as an emergency specialist, and as a supervisor of the intern training program. That was my second contract in the country, I had also worked there more than a decade earlier.

Fatima: One of my colleagues called me. Everyone rushed to grab the equipment required for resuscitation. Bag and mask ventilation and chest compressions were commenced. A cardiac monitor was attached, revealing a shockable rhythm.

Brady: A myocardial infarction – heart attack – is a medical emergency. It occurs when one of the blood vessels supplying the heart muscle becomes blocked. Urgent treatment is required to reopen the obstructed artery and prevent the heart muscle from dying.

While the heart is starved of blood, abnormal heart rhythms can occur. These are often fatal. For patients in this situation, rapid administration of chest compressions and defibrillation (an electrical shock) can be lifesaving.

Fatima: The patient was shocked with 200 joules. CPR continued for about five minutes and then she started breathing, laboured breathing. The ECG machine showed a STEMI and, thanks to our recent ELSi training, we knew that streptokinase was the drug of choice for our patient.

Brady: Restoring blood flow to the heart muscle is essential. This can be achieved with 'clot-busting' drugs. These powerful medications are potentially lifesaving but, if used inappropriately, can lead to fatal bleeding. They are also very expensive.

During my time working in Kiribati, we did not have access to these medications. But in the few days prior to the course, I had met with staff in the hospital pharmacy to see what had changed. They now had streptokinase.

When we arrived at the emergency department, we could see that our patient's condition had improved. The doctors and nurses had done a fantastic job.

ABOVE: Patients at Tungaru Central Hospital.

Even though the medication had arrived, there were no treatment guidelines in place to ensure safe use, and staff were unaware of its availability. I worked closely with the local staff to develop a protocol to suit local requirements, and then incorporated this into a stand-alone teaching session in the ELSi course. We also taught resuscitation and defibrillation.

When we arrived at the emergency department, we could see that our patient's condition had improved. The doctors and nurses had done a fantastic job. All that was left was to use the new streptokinase protocol. We showed everyone where the medication was, and then stepped them

through the administration process. We talked through what to watch out for, and how to manage any complications.

Fatima: That whole week all junior doctors received a crucial course, refreshing our knowledge of CPR, taught by an Australian emergency medical team.

After the patient's breathing had improved, I hurriedly called Dr Brady on the phone for advice on further management. He told me to look for streptokinase in the pharmacy, guiding me on the phone. He was the only one who knew where it was. That was amazing.

Not an hour after, he arrived with his team. I felt excited, deep inside. I was like, 'Oh, thank you Lord!' It was cool to be with people with great skills and knowledge who were ready to lend a hand at all times. Automatically I felt at ease.

What a coincidence. Whatever had been gained from the course had been put into practice not on a lifeless mannequin but a real patient.

My sincere thanks to the emergency nurses, Dr Brady and his team for their big contribution in saving another precious life. A sleepless night was worth it.

ABOVE: A small village on Tarawa Island in Kiribati.

Brady: Two weeks later, I was back in my usual hospital, dealing with the grind of routine work and an overflowing inbox. I noticed an email from Fatima:

Mauri Dr Brady,

I would like to say a big thank you to you and your team for your ongoing support teaching the ELSi course which gives us more confidence and competency in approaching any patient that comes to the emergency department.

Thank you very much Brady for helping me manage my STEMI patient using streptokinase. This is my first case of cardiac arrest who is alive, and it is the first time that streptokinase has been used in Kiribati and that makes me even happier. The next day the patient was awake asking her daughter, 'Wasn't I dead already?' Automatically my eyes filled with tears ... tears of happiness ... if you were not here maybe I might have lost her ...

You are so smart, clever, always ready to help, have excellent skills in teaching, and have a sense of humour. All of us junior doctors really admire you and wish that we can be like you one day. I wish that you worked here in the emergency department and be our head of department so that we can learn a lot from you.

Thanks again Brady and looking forward to meeting you with your family in the near future.

Regards,

Fatima

> "
> Tears filled my eyes. There are some emails you keep forever, in your heart as well as your inbox.

Tears filled my eyes. There are some emails you keep forever, in your heart as well as your inbox.

Reflecting on this case, what did I learn? Short courses taught by visiting faculty are often criticised for lack of applicability, either due to different epidemiology, resources or norms of practice. The lack of knowledge of local processes by educators and lack of trust among learners in the relevance of the content, can blunt effectiveness. I frequently reflect on some of the teaching sessions I have sat through in my own hospital, and how I have walked out thinking, 'That was interesting, but it isn't going to work here'.

In Kiribati, we managed to turn that around. We had a course optimised for the Pacific, and modules that were selected and then modified on site to match local needs and resources. We also had a strong knowledge of local systems, a relationship of trust with the course participants, and a deep and abiding love of the country and its people. When combined with the enthusiasm and aptitude of clinicians like Fatima, this approach has proved to be a recipe for success. •

An i-Kiribati man seeks
healthcare on remote
Abaiang Island.

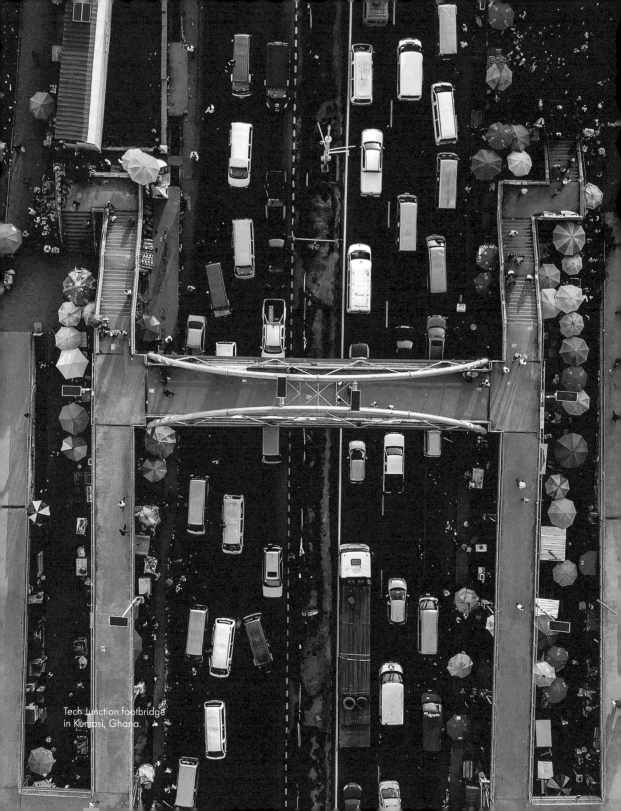

Tech Junction footbridge
in Kumasi, Ghana.

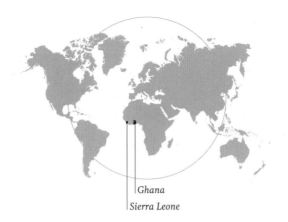

Ghana
Sierra Leone

From midnight to the dawn of a new era

JOSEPH BONNEY

Joseph Bonney is an emergency medicine specialist at Komfo Anokye Teaching Hospital in Kumasi, Ghana. He has masters degrees in public health and disaster medicine and is a research fellow with the Global Health and Infectious Diseases Research Group at the Kumasi Centre for Collaborative Research in Tropical Medicine in Ghana.

It was a few minutes to midnight and my last night in Cape Coast. My emergency medicine colleague, Eszter, the only specialist in Ghana's Central Region, which has a population of almost three million, had gone home. She had worked the entire day, but then come down with a fever and flu-like symptoms. She needed to rest.

I was driving back to my accommodation at the Cape Coast university campus, 15 minutes away from the Cape Coast Teaching Hospital, when I saw an out-of-control car speeding towards the university entrance. I was forced to stop about 50 metres away to avoid being hit. The fast-moving vehicle hit the university's marble entrance sign and then crashed loudly into a six-metre ditch.

The security personnel at the entrance ran to assess the situation. It was too dark to visualise anything, and they radioed in for assistance. I turned my car slowly to angle my headlight at the ditch to produce some illumination. In the poorly lit environment, we all froze at the extent of damage to the car. It was now upside down and there were four passengers trapped in its mangled remains. 'Omo awu anaa?' the old security man asked in Twi to find out if they were alive. There was slight movement and blinking from the driver. The arrival of the truck with three security personnel gave us the hope we needed to move in to rescue the victims. They were alive, but there was no way to assess the degree of their injuries.

What was I doing in Cape Coast, more than 200 kilometres from my home and the Komfo Anokye Teaching Hospital in Kumasi where I worked, on that day four years ago? My colleagues and I had put together a five-day disaster medicine course and were delivering it across the country. We had run the course in Kumasi, in central Ghana, and Tamale in the north. Cape Coast was our third stop before going off to the country's capital, Accra. So far, we had introduced disaster medicine to more than 150 health workers.

Our disaster medicine course had involved a live simulation exercise, so I was able to quickly grab some gloves and face masks from my car trunk and hand them to about 12 good Samaritans who were now on the scene. I was the only medic on site, so I needed to assert some authority and warn them: 'Stabilise the neck! Be careful not to cause more injury. Slow down!' My instructions fell on deaf ears. Their primary goal was to get the passengers out of the very damaged car, out of the marshy ditch, and to safety.

> My instructions fell on deaf ears. Their primary goal was to get the passengers out of the very damaged car, out of the marshy ditch, and to safety.

Wait, why was I the only medic on site? Several minutes after the incident, a call was made to the National Ambulance Service. The call was pleasantly received by dispatch, but we were told that the only ambulance available was already en route to attend to another emergency.

We managed to get three of the patients out of the car, which was still upside down. Further efforts were needed to overturn the car to get the last victim out just as the fire service arrived. Breath sounds and pulses for all four victims were very encouraging. Three of them were conscious and complaining about their pain. My scene triage placed three patients as 'red' and one as 'yellow'. Without hesitation and now listening to my guidance, the helpers now placed the victims in the security pick-up truck, which sped off to the Cape Coast Teaching Hospital.

'My job is done', I thought, relieved that I had helped expedite their trauma care. Then I recalled that Eszter was not well and all four patients

ABOVE: Ambulances of the National Ambulance Service in Ghana in front of the emergency directorate of the Komfo Anokye Teaching Hospital.

were heading her way. I had no choice but to call her to get the emergency department ready and prepared. Her voice in response was weak, but she was able to alert the emergency department staff about the cases to expect with the brief history I had given her. I followed the truck directly to the emergency unit. The night staff were fully prepared to receive the patients. It is always easy to recognise an adrenaline-pumped emergency physician, so my introduction and assumption of the role of team leader came naturally and, hopefully, had nothing to do with my loud voice.

Initial assessment showed various degrees of injuries. One patient had head and chest injuries. Others had reduced levels of consciousness, abdominal pain, lacerations and abrasions and open limb fractures.

'Can I get the ultrasound please?' The look from the nurse-in-charge quickly made me aware of my environment. My own 100-bed capacity emergency medicine directorate in Kumasi is the biggest emergency centre in Ghana and, at the time, it was the only emergency medicine residency training facility in West Africa. 'The ultrasound is not available at night, doctor', the nurse replied. Instead, we had to rely on our clinical judgement and make rapid decisions about the management of these patients.

Over the next two hours of cervical spine collars, chest tubes, IV lines, blood transfusions, long-bone fracture splinting, suturing, repeated reassessment and vital sign monitoring, the emergency team was quite comfortable that most of their patients were in a stable condition. I was at peace to leave them with the medical officers on night duty to continue management.

ABOVE: Busy traffic at Adum in Kumasi.

My mother and father were doctors. I used to watch my father work 24-hour shifts for days in a row. He was the only doctor at St Michael's Hospital in Pramso in Ghana's Ashanti Region. Travelling to work took many hours on a terrible road from our home in Kumasi. Nevertheless, I concluded when I was quite young that I wanted to help others. I am proud to be one of the 50 fully locally trained emergency medicine specialists in Ghana, a country with a population of more than 30 million people.

After I completed my residency in emergency medicine, my interest in disaster medicine led me to enrol in a master's program with CRIMEDIM – the Center for Research and Training in Disaster Medicine, Humanitarian Aid and Global Health, University of Eastern Piedmont in Italy. These paths led me to join my team from CRIMEDIM and Doctors in Africa CUAMM (Collegues Universitaires Aspirants et Médecins Missionnaires) on a mission to support the establishment of an ambulance service in Sierra Leone, Freetown.

I was the first and only Ghanaian at the start of the project and had many aims, including designing a training curriculum, authoring a training manual, preparing training material and implementing the first training course in my country. I had a lot to prove.

This was the first time I had been in another West African country, and I had travelled from Freetown to Pujehun, a border district between Sierra Leone and Liberia, where we were having our first training.

During the 312-kilometre journey to Pujehun, I pondered the development of emergency medicine in Africa. Over my few years in the emergency care field, I have seen an increase in the training programs and the effort of countries to establish both in-hospital and out of hospital emergency care.

> **With strong will and collaboration, emergency care by Africans, for Africans, is ready to save lives across our vast continent.**

Four years ago, I didn't get an ambulance that evening in Cape Coast. But now, the development of emergency medicine across the whole sub-Saharan region has seen great improvements. Ghana has developed a very strong National Ambulance Service with more than 360 ambulances at over 180 ambulance stations. It has the expertise to support the setup of the national ambulance service in other countries, too.

Today, on an early morning in 2021, as I pulled over to the side of the road to allow two blue-light ambulances to drive by, I was excited to see a pop-up on my phone showing increasing interest in emergency medicine. Fifteen doctors had just passed the exams to commence their formal specialist training in emergency medicine.

There are now more than 50 emergency medicine specialists scattered across the length and breadth of the country, 200 emergency nurses and more than 3000 emergency medical technicians. It surprises me sometimes to recall that emergency medicine in Ghana is barely 11 years old. I am a proud founding member of the two-year-old Emergency Medicine Society of Ghana, and current Vice President of the African Federation of Emergency Medicine.

The emergency medicine sector in Ghana has greatly improved to provide care not only for Ghanaians but also to export our expertise through online and physical means to support other countries during the COVID-19 pandemic as it ravages the world.

There are many challenges in research, education and clinical care; but with strong will and collaboration, emergency care by Africans, for Africans, is ready to save lives across our vast continent. •

Urban congestion in Pakistan.

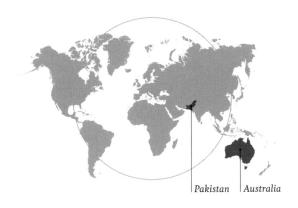

Pakistan | *Australia*

A shared journey
to success

LAI HENG FOONG

Lai Heng Foong is a senior emergency physician based in southwest Sydney and
is passionate about public health, disaster preparedness, climate change and health,
Indigenous health and the social determinants of health.

Loaded with authority letters, invitation letters and course documents, I landed in Islamabad for the first Emergency Life Support (ELS) course in Pakistan with a large mannequin in my luggage. It was challenging to explain to airport officials what the big box contained. But after some moments of tension, there was solace in being met at the airport by our gracious hosts with a garland of flowers. After a long journey, the scent of tuberose was a welcome distraction from the crowds and the chaos.

Confrontingly, our entry to the hotel was blocked by a makeshift barricade of shipping containers stacked three-high, and a heavy police presence. It was October 2018 and protests were being held following the Pakistan Supreme Court's acquittal of Christian woman Asia Bibi on charges of blasphemy. The hotel was just streets away from the Parliament of Pakistan and the court and, with security on high alert, our vehicle was inspected for bombs and all our belongings (including the mannequin) were passed through x-ray before we were allowed to enter our hotel.

The sense of unease was quickly quelled by the thrill of a new city and country. Our hosts, Abdus Salam Khan, the softly spoken President of the Pakistan Society for Emergency Medicine, and the then PSEM Vice President Junaid Mustafa (who is now its President), appeared unperturbed by the chaos around us. Junaid rallied his team and our bleary-eyed Australian team of emergency physicians into a convoy of cars and led the way up a winding road to a local hill-top restaurant. As we looked to the city below, police blockades juxtaposed with the festive atmosphere inside the restaurant. We were to encounter many more contrasts as we shared ELS skills and knowledge during our time in Pakistan.

A devastating loss

After many years of effort to start a training program at Aga Khan University Hospital in Karachi, emergency medicine emerged as a specialty recognised by the College of Physicians and Surgeons in Pakistan in 2011. In 2012 the Karachi hospital was one of just two in Pakistan, the other was Shifa International Hospital in Islamabad. The pathway to today's 13 recognised emergency departments and a system of growing international respect has occurred through the work and determination of many dedicated people.

At the penultimate moment, the venture was threatened by a country in protest and lockdown, chanting mobs and roadblocks.

For Junaid and many of his colleagues, the personal journey began with a devastating earthquake in Muzaffarabad in Kashmir in 2005. Villages vanished under the mountain; 86,000 people lost their lives, similar numbers were injured, and millions were displaced. Junaid lost 35 family members, including his brother. A British national, Junaid was specialising in internal medicine in the United Kingdom. In the aftermath of the earthquake, he immediately flew to Pakistan and the affected area to rescue and help his family. He still vividly recalls the injured students in his cousin's classroom and being forced to amputate limbs in a desperate attempt to save their lives. He returned to the United Kingdom two months later and, after a senior colleague helped him to recognise that he had suffered post-traumatic stress, resolved to change his specialisation to emergency medicine.

From the beginning, PSEM's goals have included national-level initiatives to improve access to emergency care, improve public sector emergency departments, increase training opportunities, and institute

ABOVE: Lai Heng Foong (second from right) and Pakistani emergency care colleagues deliver a training course.

a national triage system. The organisation also worked to develop a robust and relevant emergency medicine curriculum. ELS, with its focus on resource-limited environments and rural and regional areas, was to provide training to frontline healthcare workers in less supported environments. Abdus and Junaid ensured that from ELS's inception, emergency physicians and senior trainees joined as training facilitators, promoting local leadership and collaboration. The ELS program was more than simply an avenue for technical skills, but a means to create meaningful relationships and value for emergency medicine in Pakistan.

But, at the penultimate moment, the venture was threatened by a country in protest and lockdown, chanting mobs and roadblocks. Would the carload full of mannequins and equipment arrive in time?

A fortunate encounter

Farida Khawaja, a Pakistani-born FACEM (Fellow of ACEM) based in Tasmania, who had walked into Junaid's department with her sister in 2015, was integral in the development of the ELS program in Pakistan. From that fortuitous meeting she visited several times a year and worked

with Junaid and his PSEM colleagues to run small group courses in Islamabad. The arrival of the Australian team was the culmination of years of preparation by PSEM to launch ELS training in Pakistan.

ABOVE: Lai Heng Foong during a visit to Pakistan.

Through fundraising efforts in Alice Springs on the other side of the world, donations and small grants, Farida raised the money to purchase the quality mannequins needed to conduct ELS training. On the day our course was to begin, nerves quelled by 'Inshallah', God willing, from the Pakistani team, she worked with a friend and former military ambulance driver, to get the precious equipment from Sialkot to Islamabad. Farida called friends at stops along the way to provide a haven for the driver as he travelled through roadblocks made by protestors with concrete pipes, logs and burning tyres. The tension was heightened when a mobile phone blockade prevented him from letting Farida know he was safe. Forty-four hours later, to our enormous relief, he arrived with no time to spare as the first day of the course began.

The whole team, Australian and Pakistani counterparts, were keen to meet and get to know one another. Farida's team building exercise was the perfect approach to start the day, though it was a risk, given the different perspectives of the group. Dispensing with the didactic and hierarchical, we all sat in a circle, and Farida passed out coloured pipe cleaners. 'Use your imagination,' she said, 'to make something that represents a hobby that excites you outside of work'. Laughter prevailed, tensions released, and conversations began as our humanness was revealed, along with pipe cleaner violins, poetry, television and books.

Climbing mountains

For our second course, our convoy of cars loaded with mannequins, volunteer co-instructors and 'no objection' certificates (needed for foreigners to pass through the military check posts), ventured closer to the Indian border on our way to Muzaffarabad in Kashmir. The road wound through hair-pin bends and we made our way up steep, snow-covered mountains. We marvelled at the life around us. Children in blue-and-white uniforms, their heavy school bags hanging off the sides of vans on their way home. Colourful painted trucks, each one reflecting the artistic sensibilities of its owner. Yet, the emotional and physical scars of the 2005 earthquake served as poignant reminders of the value of emergency medicine and why we advocate for coordinated disaster responses.

> " The arrival of the Australian team was the culmination of years of preparation by PSEM to launch ELS training in Pakistan.

A roadside lunchtime interlude sitting on plastic tables and chairs crowded at the edge of a cliff next to a ravenous river was a highlight. We delighted in freshly prepared karahi, tandoori roti and naan and were mesmerised by the perfection of the rotis as they were pulled from a huge, hot earthen oven by the baker's bare hands.

After a late arrival in Muzaffarabad, we awoke the following morning to majestic snow-covered peaks, glistening in the morning sun. At a rich breakfast of puris, halva and curries, Farida waited for the right moment to remind us that we were now in a more conservative region and should remain discreet and quiet in public. She had already received several calls from military intelligence about our presence. Unknown and invisible 'officers' questioned the presence of foreigners and wanted details on the phone, which she refused to provide pending personally viewing written requests.

Our training venue was a new hospital built by the German government on the remains of the Muzaffarabad hospital destroyed in the earthquake. It symbolised a new frontier in emergency care in Pakistan. The infrastructure now existed, but training, systems, referral pathways, and triage were lacking.

Junaid's work in the region had built trust and introduced the concept of triage. The district chief of health endorsed the local course and provided venue and logistical support. He also helped to bring in medical officers working in community health centres and rural hospitals from remote valleys across the region. Some female medical officers had to navigate complex childcare needs to join the course and a local paediatrician arrived with a mannequin he had made to train his staff, fashioned from a life-size baby doll with lungs made from a football bladder. His ingenuity and determination to make a difference were humbling.

Our local participants took a little time to become comfortable with the friendly and familiar style of Australian emergency medicine. But by the end of the first day, thanks to our PSEM colleagues, participants were engaged in robust discussions and hands-on practice, as we adapted to their specific needs, such as adding Basic Life Support to the course. There was easy laughter when the participants realised we were all in this together.

Into the future

This opportunity to gain and share knowledge and see contrasting methods of operation was both worthwhile and enjoyable for our local medical officers, and the Australian contingent, too. It tested our boundaries and invited us all to lean into our fears and assumptions. Above all, it was an opportunity to learn as much as we taught.

The generosity, hospitality and commitment to improving emergency care in Pakistan by leaders such as Junaid is humbling.

ELS's strength is in training small groups, with an emphasis on hands-on practice and adaptability to local clinical contexts. Our Australian team had adapted the program based on feedback from Pakistani doctors and regional prevalence changing topics to focus on diabetic, cardiac, and neonatal emergencies plus locally prevalent poisonings and envenomations.

The generosity, hospitality and commitment to improving emergency care in Pakistan by leaders such as Junaid is humbling. We truly appreciated how he constantly went the extra mile to share his love for Pakistan and its people. A memorable side trip to Pir Chinasi, a narrow mountain pass at 2900 metres above sea level, was one of many opportunities to share food and immerse ourselves in this beautiful country.

The struggle to continue to advance emergency care in Pakistan will require stamina and focus.

Together, FACEMs and the PSEM team of emergency specialists and trainees from Islamabad, Peshawar, Lahore and Karachi have delivered the ELS course in Islamabad, Muzaffarabad, Lahore, Gujrat, Multan and Muzaffargarh since that first course in 2018. The many opportunities to work together towards a shared vision, while navigating uncertainties, curve balls, and sharing in the joy of food, fashion, arts, history and politics, has forged many friendships and hope for improved emergency care in Pakistan.

Emergency medicine is now recognised as a speciality in Pakistan, but the opportunities for study and professional development remain few. The trainees we worked with were at crossroads, making many pragmatic, ethical and moral choices to be able to live their dreams.

The struggle to continue to advance emergency care in Pakistan will require stamina and focus. The dedication of many FACEMS and Pakistani emergency physicians, and their support teams, have made the delivery of the ELS program a possibility. I felt grateful to be part of the love and passion for emergency care nurtured by local pioneers. Their dedication to support one another, advocate and volunteer time, expertise, and resources was, and remains, inspiring. ●

ACKNOWLEDGEMENTS

This article was written with support and feedback from Farida Khawaja and Junaid Mustafa.

Junaid Mustafa was the faculty head of the College of Physicians and Surgeons of Pakistan (CPSP) from 2015 to 2018. He is the President of the Pakistan Society of Emergency Medicine.

Farida Khawaja grew up in Pakistan and has spent the last 15 years running health-related projects in her home country from her base in Australia.

Thanks also to Fiona Reilly who was part of the Pakistan FACEM contingent that provided editorial assistance and facilitated the realisation of our vision.

All those who contributed to this article acknowledge colleagues from other countries and organisations that are supporting emergency care development in Pakistan through partnerships with PSEM.

A tricycle, known as a pedicab, drives down a street in Dumaguete, Philippines.

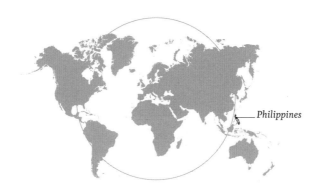

Philippines

Nearly morning

MARIA SALUD LOREEN CADIZ-KERN

Loreen Cadiz-Kern started her career as an errand kid in medical missions before becoming a volunteer nurse in a provincial emergency room in Dumaguete, Philippines. Now an emergency medicine physician trained in a public hospital, her goal is to make emergency care accessible and socially responsive.

It was one of those rare moments in our hot, crowded emergency room when things were quiet. The resuscitation bay had just two patients waiting to be transferred to the emergency department's acute care unit and join the 80 or so already stretching its 56-bed capacity. It was the kind of Sunday afternoon on which Filipino families would be sharing an extended lunch or enjoying a siesta (a holdover from three centuries of Spanish rule).

The commotion at the emergency room door wasn't unusual, but then a young man appeared, carrying a motionless body in a dress, covered in blood. We rushed to the patient, who had no pulse, and the trainee immediately started chest compressions. I don't remember how long we tried to save her life, but the rest of the story has stayed with me.

The woman, in her 70's, was the young man's grandmother. She lived with his family in their small shack built of cardboard and scrap metal and had been sitting on her small wooden stool, in her usual spot, just outside the door. Their shanty town was always busy, and she liked to watch people walk by. The rest of the family was inside, just metres away, when they heard a loud bang. 'Loud bangs' had been happening more frequently in their area. They rushed outside to see their matriarch on the ground, with blood oozing from her head.

'Single gunshot wound to the occipital area', I wrote down in my trauma sheet. Later, the police arrived at the emergency department. They said the grandmother was involved in illegal drugs and that a rival had shot her. But, of course, there were no witnesses. This wasn't unusual – there had been several reports of extrajudicial killings of people in the news around that time.

More family members arrived, crying, and the young man who brought his grandmother in sat across from us shaking his head. He asked, 'How could this happen to my *lola*? She didn't deal with drugs.' I didn't have any answers for his questions. But there was no time to help them process what had happened, or to debrief. Before I could talk to the rest of the family, two new patients arrived, and I had to go see them. Silently, I wished there was some time or space to breathe – to process the experience. But debriefs didn't happen for us. Sometimes, we got the chance to talk about events during a rushed meal, vent to another colleague, or laugh at our predicaments. At dawn, sometimes, hunched over the desks in the treatment areas, we catch short naps – after patients have been seen and procedures are complete. Then, I wait for that very brief lull between dawn and the first light outside the emergency room glass windows. If we're lucky that night, our team has time to eat breakfast and chat; just before our shift changes –when it is nearly morning.

My mother's legacy

'Your scrubs are drying on the balcony', my mother said to me in Cebuano, our native language. I opened my eyes and winced at the sunlight through the windows of my tiny, rented flat in Manila. 'She's only been here for a day and she's already cleaning up the mess', I thought. I had soaked the scrubs but was too tired to hand-wash them when I arrived home late from my shift at the hospital. My mother visited me anytime she wanted; occasionally I invited her. I had left our hometown and insisted on training here against her wishes, so it was difficult to admit that sometimes I needed her presence.

As I pondered my own challenges, I wondered how my mother had dealt with hers, and whether mine even compared. When she was my age and working as a general practitioner at a 300-bed public hospital

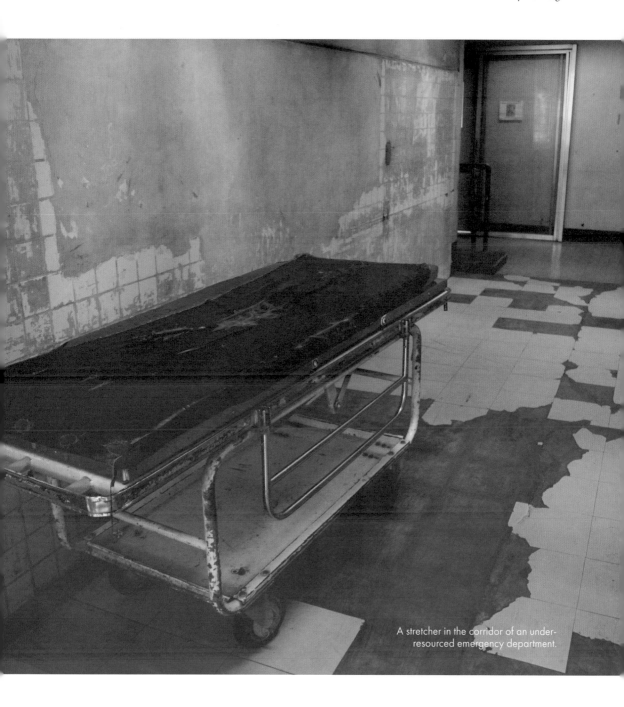

A stretcher in the corridor of an under-resourced emergency department.

in a small city in the central Philippines, she had two toddlers and juggled 30-hour shifts. She worked in this role for decades, with very low pay. Sometimes she'd donate her hard-earned money to buy a meal for a patient's family member. In some public hospitals, family members are allowed to stay at the bedside, even in the ICU. Family were 'extra' eyes and ears. They were much-needed help because of the lack of equipment and the chronic understaffing. Staff turnover was frequent due to the decades-long brain drain of clinicians to high-income countries. I wondered whether my prayerful mother's deep sense of faith sometimes helped her to sense when her once-resolute child needed support.

'What did she have Mami?', my eight-year-old self would ask over lunch while chewing a mouthful of rice. My mother would tell me her patients' stories. I loved hearing them – they always began with a question, a difficult decision, and there was always a resolution – they either died or went home. Doctors in our culture play a pivotal role that extends into patients' homes. Despite how overworked they were, my mother's generation of doctors, still had time beyond the hospital. Phrases like 'burnout' or 'moral injury' didn't exist, and they worked hard, kept their heads down, and never complained – or they'd lose their jobs.

> Phrases like 'burnout' or 'moral injury' didn't exist, and they worked hard, kept their heads down, and never complained – or they'd lose their jobs.

I realised my generation's many privileges – accessibility to resources, more livable wages, more open social support – personal or social media through apps, more approachable residency mentors and more. Still, in the spirit of soldiering on, I hadn't told my mother that I contracted pneumonia halfway through the first year of my training.

Challenges of my own

It was a week into the new year, and I was the most junior emergency trainee in the department. There were only two other trainees on that shift, one was triaging and helping me, and the other was on her rounds. My cough had been going on for two weeks. I had bought my own nebuliser and used it in the on-call room during breaks. A senior colleague had made a joke about getting a chest x-ray and checking for tuberculosis (TB) and we laughed that I might have to buy my own oxygen tank as the department had run out of oxygen two days earlier.

A few days later it got worse. I needed to take five days off and spent

ABOVE: An ambulance van belonging to the Philippine Red Cross.

three of them as an inpatient. Another senior trainee later told me that those five days would be counted as vacation. I was surprised – was this how it worked? Sick days were vacation days? I went to my training consultant who said, 'No. Sick days are not vacation days.' I recovered and, luckily, I didn't get that sick again, even though we routinely intubated patients without masks or face shields and occasionally ran out of PPE. But I suffered daily stomach cramps every time I walked the two blocks from home to work.

My fellow trainees and I often talked about our stress-related ailments. The residency attrition rate was more than 50 per cent. We knew this – no-one had ever painted a pretty picture of residency – and it helped to talk to one another. But often our seniors pushed us out of necessity. I was asked to start doing second-year tasks halfway through my first year. I wasn't alone, we all stepped up (or tried to) when we were asked.

For as long as we had our friends and great food, we coped. One of my favourite times on shift was at 5am. Nearly morning, it meant sharing breakfast, stories and iced coffee with my colleagues. And of course, the next team arriving to relieve us soon.

Breaking point

Our public hospital training taught us a code of 'service-first'. Patient numbers would double, or even triple our capacity, yet we were still expected to show up. Exams and lectures could be cancelled, research papers delayed, but shifts couldn't be. Several times, we extended our shifts when someone was late or absent. We had to pull together, carry on. The only thing that helped me survive my second year of training was the knowledge that I wasn't alone in my misery. Complain, but do it. Sometimes I felt too angry to pity myself or cry.

I was on hour 28, post-shift, but still needed to take an exam. As I made my way to the exam room, I saw a young man in the hallway, laying on a stetcher in restraints, with dark stains all over his clothes. He spat out a charcoal slurry. An attending physician passed by and noticed his agitation and partial state of undress. She found a blanket and covered him for some privacy. He calmed down. I looked away, thinking he wasn't my patient, so I wasn't responsible for him. Yet a deep, uncomfortable feeling gnawed at me. How did I ignore him when I walked by last night? Did my busyness excuse me? There was no clinical consequence, he was discharged the next day. It was no big deal. Was I over-internalising? Yet the feeling of shame persisted. When did my sense of dignity die?

> Was I over-internalising? Yet the feeling of shame persisted. When did my sense of dignity die?

The next day after showering and changing, I couldn't leave the apartment. I had endured many days like this before, but I always made it to work. I asked one of my colleagues to 'just give me a few days and I'll be back'. 'OK, but we will be checking on you', she said. I messaged my consultant with an apology. Two of my fellow trainees met up with me some days later. They told me that they didn't expect me to get to this breaking point, although several others had done so already. It was like a rite of passage. They thought I was doing OK.

A week later, I met with my consultant. She told me that I was the 'last one standing', and said she never thought I'd break too. There had been seven trainees in my group at the start of the year. Six months later, I joined the remaining three. At any point of our training program, it was an understanding that some of us would reach low points; some take a break and return, and some never do. I didn't want to quit the program. I held back my tears. I told her I wasn't the same person who could hear out an angry patient or family and find a way to work with them. I was afraid that being impatient would lead to poor patient care, and maybe already had. I wasn't the same person who confidently made clinical decisions. I was full of doubt when there was an undesired outcome. I felt shame when I remembered an old mentor's praise for me. I felt shame when I remembered my own mother's voice when I was nine years old and complaining while following her on rounds: 'Be kind to the patients. They are in more discomfort than you are.'

The consultant was surprised that I worried about these things. She advised me to compartmentalise my concerns. I also worried whether taking this leave would mean extending my training. She said, 'No, this will count as a sick leave', and that I didn't need to make up for the time. This surprised me, instead of dismissing my concerns she validated them. In a culture where non-stop work and patient loads were bragging rights, 'taking a break' was a weakness. But for the first time, the consultant didn't make me feel that it was.

My experience wasn't unique. It was common and even worse in some hospitals. We heard anecdotes of trainees in other specialties who abruptly left their programs because they had no other option. Some were found unresponsive in their beds.

Service first

In my final year, I juggled the last six months of training as a third-year trainee and also served my peers in a broader leadership role. When fellow trainees went through their own breaking points, the consultants gave them time. We were careful not to pressure any of them to stay, or to feel guilty if they chose to leave. Some have thanked us and carried on, some have left. We have referred others to professional help for mental health. I hope we did right by all of them. My original group graduated ahead of me, but I later followed them.

When the pandemic restricted travel in the Philippines, I was on a dawn flight to work at another frontline. As supplies of protective equipment dwindled, I trusted that my former colleagues, being used to scarcity, would adapt as they always have. It has gone far longer than we thought, and loss and grief have touched us all.

In time, the worn scrubs and bloodstained shoes will be washed away. Meanwhile, although many of us are now working in different locations, we still check in virtually with one another. In this safe space, we wait until it's nearly morning so we can share breakfast, stories, and welcome the new team. ●

An island off the northern coast of Papua New Guinea.

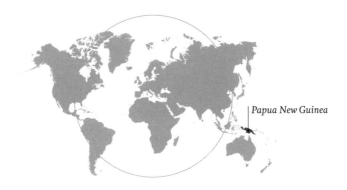

Papua New Guinea

Calm amid the chaos

WILMA SEBBY

Wilma Sebby is a senior emergency nurse in Papua New Guinea (PNG). She is the nurse unit manager of the ANGAU Memorial Provincial Hospital's emergency department in Lae.

The emergency department at ANGAU Memorial Provincial Hospital (AMPH) in Lae is small and run down. There are not enough staff and we do not have enough resources. Sometimes there are only one or two nurses working on each shift, so our patients wait on the deck outside for hours. It's an unpredictable place. It's like having a tiger creeping up to pounce on its prey - it can be calm one minute, and chaos the next.

When the place is calm it's frightening too, because we know that anything can happen at any time. So we stock the shelves, we clean up, we stay alert, and we prepare for whatever we must face next. When a trauma or an unwell patient comes in, the chaos starts. It becomes crowded and noisy, often there are people crying in pain, fighting, or yelling, sometimes visitors are wailing to signal the loss of a recently passed relative, and sometimes there are sirens indicating an incoming emergency. The smell is another thing we must always be prepared for - whether it's sweat, blood, urine, faeces, vomit, or sometimes a mix of all.

Our hospital covers a huge geographical area – from the highlands to the islands. We are surrounded by mountains and the sea, and we get a lot of rain, so it can be difficult for people to travel to the hospital. Sometimes patients travel very long distances, and by the time they arrive they are in very poor condition. At times, patients come to the emergency department at the end of their life, and we take the time to bathe them and care for them until they pass on. It gives us a feeling of satisfaction and we know in our hearts that we have done something good for them and that they have moved on to another life.

Other times, the care we provide feels less satisfying. Last year, at times our hospital ran out of essential drugs, including adrenaline. A patient arrived in cardiac arrest, and we tried to resuscitate him, but we didn't have what was needed. We watched the patient pass on before our eyes. It made us feel awful to just stand there and not be able to do anything because of all the resource constraints. Afterwards we had a debrief to share our feelings and frustrations and to give one another support. We've had to keep fighting for what we need, but luckily things have improved now so we have better supplies.

> Sometimes patients travel very long distances, and by the time they arrive they are in very poor condition.

Through a younger lens

When I was a student, I was young and energetic. I loved doing deliveries and I wanted to become a midwife. After my studies, I started work at Kundiawa Hospital in Simbu Province and I followed my dream. I liked doing all the deliveries and suturing on my own. There was nobody to supervise me, so I worked independently. Every case was a new challenge and I had to learn to adapt.

Kundiawa Hospital was really run down when I first worked there, and there was no emergency department. Each new patient went to the outpatient department to be treated or admitted. We lived in the dilapidated sisters' quarters, but we barely cared we were so grateful for the opportunity, and we wanted to start work as soon as we could. I quickly built a reputation as a hard worker and in 1996 I was chosen to travel to Lae to attend the country's first introduction to emergency care course with a small group of staff. At that time, PNG was just starting to introduce emergency departments to its hospitals, and the experience really drew me into the world of emergency nursing. I liked that you were multiskilled and got to do a little bit of everything – things never got boring. After

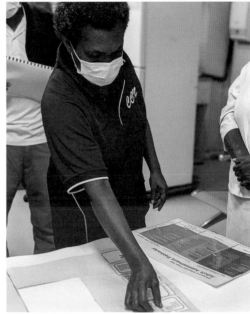

ABOVE LEFT: Staff don personal protective equipment during a COVID-19 surge in Lae, Papua New Guinea.

ABOVE RIGHT: Wilma Sebby participates in an emergency department training exercise.

a while, we moved to a new hospital built by the Japanese government, which was much better and had a small four-bed emergency department. I was later appointed as nurse unit manager of the emergency department and I worked at Kundiawa for 10 years.

I moved to Lae in 2000 to work in the AMPH emergency department. It was a huge challenge – I had never done ECGs, or ordered treatments, or medications. Eventually I became the emergency department nurse unit manager, and for many years I had no cover and no support; I had to fill the position of manager for both the nurses and the doctors. One day there was a medical symposium on in Lae, so I made myself an appointment with the chief of emergency medicine for PNG. I insisted: 'We need a medical manager here'. We got a senior doctor not long after that, and things got much better. But we have had to fight for the things we need.

Daily challenges
Sadly, COVID-19 has brought many more challenges. Our very first COVID-19 positive patient stayed in the emergency department for 10 days, because there were problems transferring to the COVID ward.

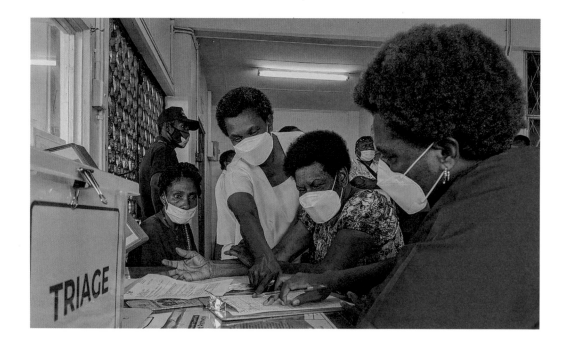

We don't have rooms for isolation here, so we had to use our resuscitation area. While things have improved, we still face many difficulties transferring patients out of the department. At first there was a shortage of supplies but now the challenges are mostly in logistics and staffing. It has been a huge burden for our team.

At the beginning, I could see the look of dread on the faces of my staff when they came to work. They were so worried about taking COVID-19 home to their families. Most of the nurses have had COVID-19 now, and some have been reinfected more than once. I worry the staff are not looking after themselves so I'm continually reminding them to sanitise and wear masks. Our staff shortages continue, but my senior nurses have stepped up and helped fill a lot of shortages.

As a manager, I have felt a lot of pressure and responsibility because all the staff look up to me to provide everything for them. I have had to give them reassurance and make sure they have what they need to keep safe at work, so that they can concentrate on their jobs. Staff need to know they have a leader who is supporting them, they have somebody they can turn to, and if something is out of stock, they know who to ask and they know I will work to get them what they need.

ABOVE: Wilma Sebby and colleagues at ANGAU Memorial Provincial Hospital discuss a new approach to triage.

Do the small things

As leaders in emergency medicine, we have to be sponges and soak everything up. I encourage my staff to continue reading, to update themselves about what's happening, and remain up to speed with the latest changes. As leaders we need to be good role models for our staff. We can't be too proud to do the small things - it can have a drastic effect on patient care. Sometimes I might help wash a patient, cut their hair, or give them a shave - it can't just be about interventions and medicines. Too often things get so busy we take a brief history and then must move on to the next patient, because there are so many more to see.

Nursing in PNG has advanced over the years. Nurses now graduate with degrees from universities thanks to our nursing leaders and educators. But some things haven't changed. To be successful, nurses must be committed, have a strong sense of duty, maintain a positive attitude towards work and continually build their knowledge and skills. Only with these attributes can we deliver quality care to our people and ensure a positive future for nursing in PNG. The challenges are never ending, but we must stay strong.

> **The wards may be full, and the emergency department may be crowded, but I'll keep doing my best to serve our patients.**

I'm always thankful that I'm a nurse taking care of people. Because it's people that matter. The wards may be full, and the emergency department may be crowded, but I'll keep doing my best to serve our patients. We can and we do make a difference. ●

ACKNOWLEDGEMENTS
Thanks go to Australian emergency nurse Sarah Bornstein for assisting with this story. The accompanying photos were taken by Jean-Philippe Miller who worked with staff at ANGAU Memorial Provincial Hospital in 2021 as part of the PNG Clinical Support Program (CSP), funded by the Australian Government through the Papua New Guinea–Australia Partnership and managed by Johnstaff International Development.

ENERAL O.P.D.

TOKSAVE 3/8/14
GO LO JORIRA
CLINIC
SAPOS U TING
U GAT
SIK MEASLES
Th

An emergency department nurse speaks
to patients awaiting care during a measles
outbreak in Papua New Guinea in 2014.

Australia's Parliament
House as seen from
bushland on Mount
Ainslie, near Canberra.

Ireland | Australia |
United Kingdom |

The forge

DAVID CALDICOTT

David Caldicott is an emergency medicine consultant who trained in the United Kingdom and Australia. He is based in Canberra, Australia, with his family.

I'm an academic brat. Not in the sense that I am in any way truly 'academic'. Far from it – or at least, not in any modern sense that might be considered as being 'useful'. No, I'm the child of academics, far brighter than myself, from the halcyon days when light-footed intellectuals could flit from one country to another, satisfying their cultural curiosities, while pursuing their careers. My childhood included the huge expanses of America's nicer northern neighbours, the densely cultured, umami-laden terroir of the Mediterranean, and a small, wet island on the westernmost edge of Europe.

Ireland is green, and for good reason. The weather from the Atlantic, brought to us exclusively from the west and laden with moisture, hops from foot to foot like a drunk in a bar with a full bladder, looking for some wall against which to splash. That wall is Ireland. We have words and ways of describing rain, in the same manner that the Inuit describe the snow. My grandfather, an elder held in the same regard as Elders in my adopted country of Australia, would speak as we walked of a 'soft day', on which the rain did not fall, but was more 'walked through', like a cloud gripping the nap of the land, before it ever had a chance to form discrete drop. It was not so much felt, as imbibed, imbued. He would delight in pointing out the gorse in flower and remind me that it was the only time of the year in which it was appropriate to kiss a girl. (Gorse, gentle reader, is always in flower in Ireland.)

Fire was not a concern, growing up – at least, and certainly not in any physical sense. It did, however, carry great portent for The Soul. Spiritually, it has always been part of Celtic ritual – fire bridges the realms of the living and the dead and protects us from The Fey. The pagan festival of Samhain, which most of the world has quaintly repackaged as Hallowe'en, represents a perilous time of the year, the moment in time where the realms of the living and the dead are most closely approximated. There were no bushfires – there is no 'bush'. Every few years, the sparks from the train down to Rosslare would ignite the heather on Bray Head, or Killiney Hill, and tufts of smoke would bravely endure, until the next deluge moved through, usually within hours. Accidental fires in Ireland are stillborn – even the soothsayer Nostradamus knew that. In the end of days, while the rest of the world is destined to burn, Ireland alone will be spared that fate – we will all be drowned.

I studied my medicine in London, in a national health service through which the first chill winds of corporatisation were beginning to blow – and fell in love with my tribe early. Jane Fothergill and Robin Touquet, monolithic figures of emergency medicine in the United Kingdom, stood astride my formative years. They taught me about patients and patience, and why we all must advocate for the ill and injured, always. It was never pitched as an optional extra to the vocation – it was integral to what we were to become.

> Fire was not a concern, growing up – at least, and certainly not in any physical sense. It did, however, carry great portent for The Soul.

Following a tectonically failed relationship, I fled the United Kingdom on the toss of a coin, between the options of the Antipodes, and trying to enlist in the French Foreign Legion, which at the time seemed roughly the equivalent to a lovelorn lonely Irishman. Within weeks of that fatal flip, I was on my way. I took my hand luggage down from the overhead locker when the captain announced we had crossed the north coast of Australia – I waited another four hours with a suitcase on my lap until we arrived

ABOVE: Fires in Namadgi Park, near Canberra, threaten suburbs and create a major air pollution risk.

in Adelaide. This was my first of many lessons provided to me by Australia – it's a much bigger island than anyone who hasn't visited can ever know.

Briefly, under the tutelage of Marie Kuhn, I found peace. She too had made her own pilgrimage before me, from working in the gun-addled world of American emergency medicine, to the relative calm of the City of Churches, before tragically being taken from us too soon. I learned peace-making and equanimity from Chris Baggoley, who later became the Chief Medical Officer of Australia. They must have seen things in me that I did not see in myself, for they tolerated my wayward character and inclination to disobedience with persistent forgiveness, while gently nudging me back on the road to progress. They taught me who I wanted to be, if ever I was to become a leader in my own right and provided me with an ember of hope that was to sustain me through a future difficult decade of medical nonconformity.

Australia is mostly not green – it's a 'sunburnt country', a 'wide, brown land'. In recent years, it's been on fire – a lot. I had heard people speak of fires in South Australia – on my forays out and about around the state 20 years on, the stories of the Ash Wednesday fires still haunted many. I recall seeing the melted chassis of a motorcycle mounted on a wall and marvelling at a destructive force that I had only seen on television.

In January 2007, I was taking the love of my life, my future wife, to meet my parents, when I had the opportunity to encounter a bushfire firsthand. I was a hill away from the Mount Bold Reservoir in South Australia when a fire broke out and howled towards us like a vengeful djinn, out of captivity, and desperate for retribution. There was no alternative for us but to hold our ground, and shelter in place – there is no out-running such creatures. That I am here to tell the tale is a phenomenon that I still don't fully understand.

I returned to the NHS, in the summer of 2009, to be closer to my family in a time of trouble. The NHS was a pale shadow of what it once was, a beautiful clipper deliberately foundered on the rocks, and being salvaged by mercenaries and privateers. I had the pleasure of working with my best man for three years, but in a system riddled with red tape and inefficiencies.

Canberra has offered me sanctuary and stoked a fire that was set in London and Adelaide. Having tested my mettle for two decades, I was allowed to hone an edge to the crude blade that my makers had forged. For a life in emergency medicine is a forge. We enter it, hoping that we will emerge, tempered to the tasks that face us. We are shaped by our predecessors, who have survived, who have been shaped by those who have come before them. If we are shaped by master-craftsmen, by great teachers and leaders, we may become something of worth, someone who in turn might make great blades in the name of those that taught us. The metal we are made of is as important as to how it is forged – but a great teacher can make a lasting blade from nigh on any material, with enough time and patience.

As a profession, we are increasingly being called up to return to something very old in the vocation of healing – the role of the advocate. It is something that we have collectively almost forgotten, like the hint of a tune, once sung around a fire. We have been exhorted to 'stay in our lanes' by those who have transgressed into ours and threatened with consequences should we not comply. It is always easier to comply when threatened by those in authority, but if I have learned anything in my journey so far, it is that doing the right thing in medicine is almost never

For a life in emergency medicine is a forge. We enter it, hoping that we will emerge, tempered to the tasks that face us.

the easy thing. Whether it is the treatment of refugees, inequalities in medicine, drug law reform, the mismanagement of a pandemic, or climate change, we have a vocational duty to earn the respect that we are afforded by society.

With regards to the latter, we are at an existential point of decision. In the summer of 2019-2020, as an unknown virus was beginning to make its mark in Wuhan in China, Canberra found itself surrounded by fires, smoke descending into the natural hollow that is my home. For a while, the bush capital of Australia had the worst air quality in the world. Many citizens found themselves triggered by the dense acrid smoke with memories of 2003 where, instead of choking, Canberra had burned, burned with such a vigour that the world's first 'fire tornado' was recorded. The irony that the circumstances creating the fires that ravaged the entire east coast of Australia that summer – killing billions of wild animals and destroying livelihoods and lives – were at least in part a consequence of policies of climate denial, propagated by politicians now suffocating in smoke, escaped no-one. By the time COVID-19 arrived on the scene, Canberrans were already well-used to the idea of facemasks. This was the first time I had experienced, directly, what the future might hold in store for us – for my family – should we not take a stand.

Never has the need for the medical profession to sing the song of advocacy been greater. We are at a moment of Samhain for our species – a point of inflection between a world in which we can live, and one in which we cannot. We will be judged by what we have done, as a tribe capable of doing much. Remaining silent in the face of denial, mendacity, opacity and ever-growing institutional inequality is no longer a path that can be taken by those who hold the tradition of our craft in high esteem. Our very existence as a species now rests with those prepared to speak out and become the bladesmiths that their leaders and teachers intended. •

Emergency nurse Roselyn Morribo participating
in emergency care training in Port Vila in Vanuatu.
Training was being delivered by Australian nurses
John Foley and Libby White, who were supported
by the Australian Volunteers Program to assist the
Vila Central Hospital Emergency Department.

ACKNOWLEDGEMENTS

A team of dedicated individuals across the globe have helped make *When Minutes Matter* a reality.

Our heartfelt thanks go to everyone at Hardie-Grant Publishing for assisting with this publication. An impromptu meeting over dinner in Carlton – a suburb in Melbourne, Australia – led to a productive partnership from the very beginning. We would especially like to acknowledge Courtney Nicholls and Hannah Louey for their outstanding support in coordinating the project, Leanne Tolra for her exceptional editorial guidance and Robert Bertagni for his design expertise.

We are also grateful to the International Federation for Emergency Medicine, and in particular President Sally McCarthy, for endorsing this project. IFEM support provided a strong incentive to launch *When Minutes Matter* at the International Conference on Emergency Medicine in Melbourne, June 2022. The conference theme of 'Better care for a better world' is deeply embedded in the pages of this book.

To the leadership team at the Australasian College for Emergency Medicine, thank you for supporting this concept from the outset. In particular, we would like to acknowledge the Project Management Group, comprised of Clare Skinner, John Bonning, Simon Judkins, Sally McCarthy, Peter White and Lisa English. To all members of the Project Editorial Working Group, listed below, and the broader team of writing mentors, thank you for countless hours of work in reviewing, editing and curating these stories. We are grateful for your experience, knowledge and guidance.

This project would never have succeeded without Michelle Hackney and Andrea Johnston, two incredible staff members at ACEM who have kept us on-track throughout the publication process. Michelle and AJ, you have continually amazed us with your tireless support, and we are deeply indebted to you both.

We also acknowledge the essential input provided by the ACEM Global Emergency Care Committee and Global Emergency Care Manager Sarah Korver. ACEM has a long history of supporting locally-led emergency care capacity development in partnership with governments, training institutions and clinicians. The deep commitment of the College, its fellows and its staff to universal, high quality emergency care is evidenced throughout this book.

To the authors, our global colleagues, thank you. Without your contributions, this publication would never have been possible. Thank you for bravely sharing your stories and experiences in global emergency care. And most importantly, thank you for the work you do, day in and day out – you are the proof that emergency care matters.

We also acknowledge those individuals and organisations, such as the Australian Volunteers Program and Médecins Sans Frontières, that supplied photographs for the book. Thank you for helping bring the stories to life with such poignant images.

Finally, we would like to express respect and gratitude to our patients. Thank you for trusting us with your care and allowing us to advocate on your behalf. It is a privilege to practise emergency medicine, and we hope this book goes some way to improving emergency care access and outcomes across the globe. ●

Jennifer Jamieson and Rob Mitchell
On behalf of the editorial team

Project Editorial Working Group	Writing mentors
Megan Cox	Colin Banks
Anne Creaton	Marcus Kennedy
Syed Ghazanfar Saleem	Nicholas Taylor
Sandy Inglis	Gina Watkins
Jennifer Jamieson	
Andrea Johnston	
Emefa Kporku	
Gayatri Lekshmi Madhavan	
Rob Mitchell	
Courtney Nicholls	

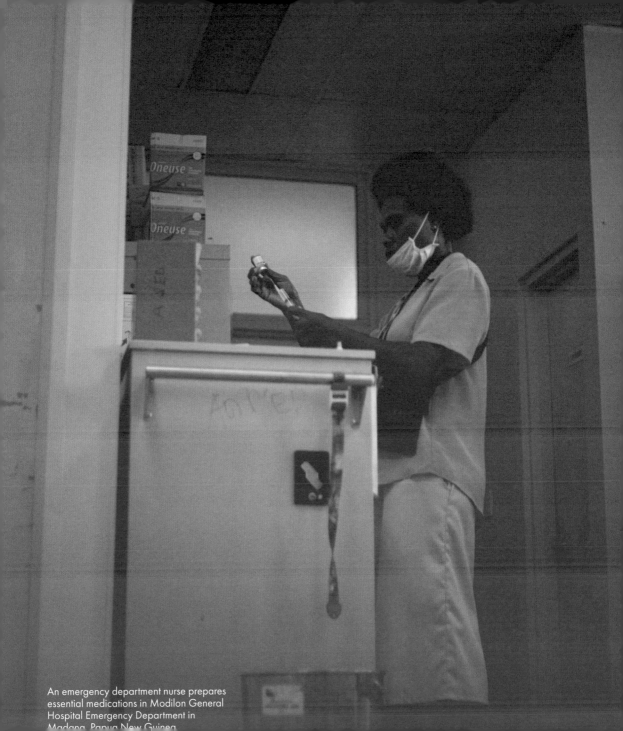

An emergency department nurse prepares
essential medications in Modilon General
Hospital Emergency Department in
Madang, Papua New Guinea.

PHOTOGRAPHY CREDITS

Aloima Taufilo pg 44–54
iStock.com/Dmitry Malov pg 44
Darren James pg 47, 48

Alphonce Simbila pg 54–61
iStock.com/Moiz Husein pg 54
Abbott Fund, 57, 58

Amaali Lokuge pg 90–97
iStock.com/David Hewison pg 90
Arjun Bhogal/The Alfred Hospital pg 93, 97
iStock.com/razaklatif pg 94

Amy Neilson pg 150–157
iStock.com/USO pg 153
Amy Neilson pg 150, 154

Ankur Verma pg 126–133
iStock.com/Wysiati pg 126,
iStock.com/anil_shakya19 pg 129

Brady Tassicker and Fatima Mwemwenikeaki
pg 184–191
iStock.com/sorincolac pg 184
Brady Tassicker pg 186–187
iStock.com/SU8Productions pg 188

David Caldicott pg 222–227
iStock.com/R Clare pg 222
iStock.com/Daniiielc pg 225

Evan O'Neill pg 78–89
iStock.com/Mondal Falgoonee Kumar pg 78
Anthony Kwan/Médecins Sans Frontières
pg 81, 82, 85, 87

Harendra Cooray pg 142–149
iStock.com/Oleh_Slobodeniuk pg 142
iStock.com/PeskyMonkey pg 145
Harendra Cooray pg 146
iStock.com/rajkobrvic pg 149

Heidi Edmundson pg 20–27
iStock.com/Mlenny pg 20
istock.com/Andrius Kaziliunas pg 23

Petra Niclasen and Ina Schapiro pg 28–35
iStock.com/fotofritz16 pg 28
Australasian College for Emergency
Medicine pg 31
iStock.com/Sam Jackson pg 32–33

Joseph Bonney pg 192–197
Gerard Nartey Photography pg 192
Joe Bonney Photography pg 195, 196

Jule Santos pg 178–183
istock.com/tirc83 pg 178
Jule Santos pg 181, 183

Justine Athieno Odakha pg 170–177
istock.com/AnjoKanFotografie pg 170
Dada Photos Lab pg 173 (left)
Darren James pg 173 (right)
istock.com/emretopdemir pg 176

Katrina Starmer pg 04–11
Ranger Dave pg 07 (left)
iStock.com/vanbeets pg 07 (right)
Russell Shakespeare pg 04, 08–09
Wendy Cannon pg 10–11

Kelly Phelps pg 98–105
Ian Benson pg 98
iStock.com/dan_prat pg 101

Killiam Argote–Aramèndiz
pg 134–141
iStock.com/Dessothompson pg 134
Killiam Argote–Aramendiz pg 137, 138

Lai Heng Foong pg 198–205
iStock.com/Hamza Dildar pg 198
Farida Khawaja pg 201, 202

Maria Salud Loreen Cadiz–Kern
pg 206–213
iStock.com/livcool pg 206
istock.com/Nattapon Malee pg 209
iStock.com/tupungato pg 211

Meg McKeown pg 70–75
iStock.com/Ray Hems pg 70
Meg McKeown pg 73
iStock.com/Miralex pg 74–75

Nada Hassan Ahmed Abdelrahman
pg 36–43
iStock.com/ferozeea pg 36
iStock.com/christophe_cerisier pg 39

**Natalie Thurtle and Mohammed Abu
Mughiasib** pg 106–117
Fady Hanona/Médecins Sans Frontières
pg 106, 109, 112
Médecins Sans Frontières pg 110, 114–115

Rosanne Skalicky pg 118–125
iStock.com/g4gary pg 118
Rosanne Skalicky pg 121
iStock.com/Maxiphoto pg 122

Sa'ad Lahri pg 12–19
iStock.com/RapidEye pg 12
Darren James pg 15, 17

Tileah Drahm–Butler pg 62–69
iStock.com/mauricallari pg 62
Australasian College for Emergency Medicine
pg 65, 66–67

Vincent Atua pg 160–169
iStock.com/mvaligursky pg 160
Niki Kuautonga/Australian Volunteers Program
pg 163
Gina Kaitiplel/Australian Volunteers Program
pg 164

Wilma Sebby pg 214–221
iStock.com/Joel Carillet pg 214
JP Miller pg 217, 218

General images various pages
istock.com/sshepard pg viii
istock.com/pixinoo pg x
Harjono Djoyobisono/Australian Volunteers
Program pg 03, 60–61
Darren James pg 18–19, 52–53, 190–191,
220–221, 231
iStock.com/Brian A Jackson pg 26–27
Fady Hanona/Médecins Sans Frontières pg 77
Hasnat Sohan/Médecins Sans Frontières
pg 88–89
The Alfred Hospital pg 104–105
Sarah Bornstein/JP Miller pg 116–117
iStock.com/Priya Darshan pg 132–133
Darren James/Australian Volunteers Program
pg 159
Niki Kuautonga/Australian Volunteers Program
pg 168–169, 228–229, 233
iStock.com/VasukiRao pg 234–235

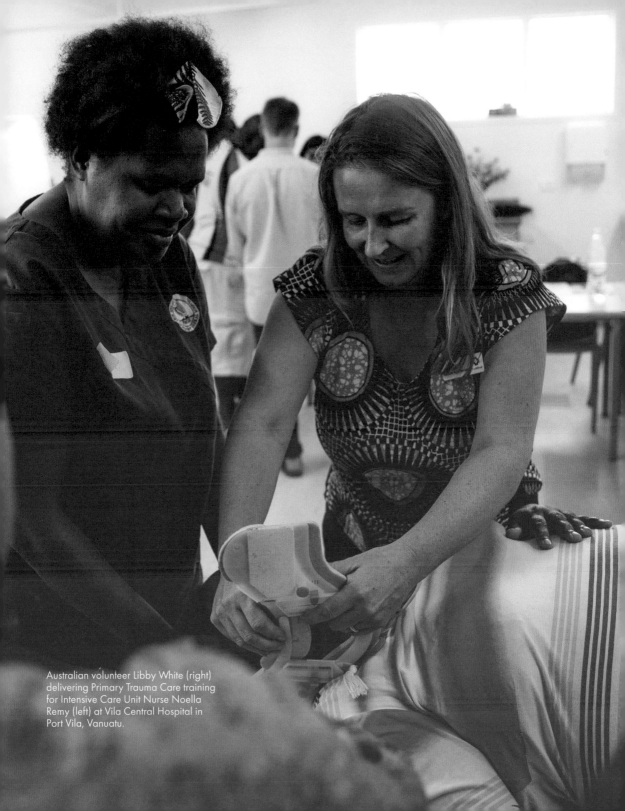

Australian volunteer Libby White (right)
delivering Primary Trauma Care training
for Intensive Care Unit Nurse Noella
Remy (left) at Vila Central Hospital in
Port Vila, Vanuatu.

Patients queue outside a Telangana state hospital in Hyderabad, India during the COVID-19 pandemic.

ABBREVIATIONS

AAD – Australian Antarctic Division
ACEM – Australasian College for Emergency Medicine
ACRRM – Australian College of Rural and Remote Medicine
AED – automated external defibrillator
AMPH – ANGAU Memorial Provincial Hospital
ATFC – Ambulatory Therapeutic Feeding Centre
CPR – cardiopulmonary resuscitation
CRIMEDIM – Center for Research and Training in Disaster Medicine, Humanitarian Aid and Global Health
CT – computerised tomography
CUAMM – Collegues Universitaires Aspirants et Médecins Missionnaires
ECG – electrocardiogram
ED – emergency department
ELS – Emergency Life Support
EM – emergency medicine
FACEM – Fellow of the Australasian College for Emergency Medicine
FOAMed – free open-access medical education
ICRC – International Committee of the Red Cross
ICU – intensive care unit
IFEM – International Federation for Emergency Medicine
IITT – Interagency Integrated Triage Tool
IV – intravenous
MRI – magnetic resonance imaging
MSF – Médecins Sans Frontières
MUAC – mid-upper arm circumference
PNG – Papua New Guinea
PPE – personal protective equipment
PSEM – Pakistan Society of Emergency Medicine
RFDS – Royal Flying Doctor Service
SAM – Society for Acute Medicine
SSCCEM – Sri Lankan Society for Critical Care and Emergency Medicine
STEMI – ST elevation myocardial infarction
TB – tuberculosis
UN – United Nations
UTI – urinary tract infection
VIP – very important person